MATING SYSTEMS, SEXUAL DIMORPHISM, AND THE ROLE OF MALE NORTH AMERICAN PASSERINE BIRDS IN THE NESTING CYCLE

BY

JARED VERNER

AND

MARY F. WILLSON

ORNITHOLOGICAL MONOGRAPHS NO. 9

PUBLISHED BY

THE AMERICAN ORNITHOLOGISTS' UNION

INTRODUCTION

The following review grew out of an analysis of polygyny in North American passerine birds (Verner and Willson, 1966). It serves as a quick reference to most of the papers dealing with nest observations in North American passerines and presents a preliminary analysis of the role of male passerines in the nesting cycle.

We had hoped that a survey of the roles of males would enable us to identify species which had hitherto been unrecognized as being polygynous. Inasmuch as males of polygynous species would normally continue to advertise for mates even though they were already mated, it seems likely that they would spend less time in such activities as nest building, incubation, and feeding young. While males of polygynous species do tend to devote less time to the various chores associated with nesting than do those of monogamous species (Tables 3 and 4), we were able to predict only one additional case of unrecognized polygyny on this basis. We suggested that the Dickcissel is polygynous (Verner and Willson, 1966) because the male reportedly does little else than sing during all phases of the nesting cycle. This has since been confirmed by Zimmerman (1966). We also believe the Short-billed Marsh Wren to be polygynous on the basis of the apparent similarity of its courting procedures with the three wrens of the temperate region that are known to be polygynous. In this review the Short-billed Marsh Wren has been included among the polygynous species. The possibility that polygyny is common in the Painted Bunting needs investigation (see Parmelee, 1959).

Although the review proved generally of little value for the original purpose, a brief glance at Table 1 indicates those species that particularly need to be studied, as well as those for which there are many studies available. All references for each species are indicated by number and may thus be quickly extracted from the bibliography. Hopefully this tabulation will be used by amateur ornithologists, graduate students, and even professionals as a guide for future studies of avian life histories. The more gaps that can be filled with meaningful, quantitative data, the more useful such a tabulation will become as a basis for generalization.

ACKNOWLEDGMENTS

Opinions regarding the extent of sexual variation of the species considered were very kindly given by Dr. D. H. Baepler, Mr. E. Eisenmann, Dr. D. A. Lancaster, Dr. R. T. Peterson, Dr. S. M. Russell, Dr. G. M. Sutton, and Dr. E. O. Willis. Drs. D. A. Lancaster and S. M. Russell provided data from unpublished theses, and Dr. N. K. Johnson assisted with evaluation of species involved in early publications on the *Empidonax griseus-oberholseri-wrightii* complex. The literature search was spread over a five-year period, during which time support was provided by NSF Predoctoral and Postdoctoral Fellowships and by NSF GB-5241.

METHODS

This section should be regarded primarily as an explanation of Table 1. Since the review was in conjunction with a study of the influence of habitats on avian mating systems, many aspects of our coverage were based on considerations of that study. Consequently, as a general review of the role of male passerines in the nesting cycle, this paper has deficiencies that would require an unwarranted amount of time to eliminate. Explanations of the various limitations and procedures employed in preparing this review follow:

1. Species recently introduced to North America, either naturally or artificially, were eliminated from consideration, since their mating systems might still reflect adjustments to habitat conditions at their point of origin and not to those in their new surroundings. Social parasites were not considered, since neither sex is involved with the usual operations of nesting. Finally, coverage was limited to species known to nest north of the northern Mexican border.

2. Species have been classed as sexually dimorphic if the sexes of fully adult birds can be unambiguously distinguished in the field during the breeding season on the basis of size and/or coloration. The extent of variation between the sexes ranges from essentially none to extreme variation, as in the Boat-tailed Grackle, and between these extremes are many species that simply cannot be categorized according to the definition given above. We considered the possibility of a third category, such as 'usually dimorphic,' to include problematical species (e.g. the Horned Lark, Barn Swallow, Red- and White-breasted nuthatches, Robin, White and Yellow wagtails, Tennessee and Magnolia warblers, Eastern and Western meadowlarks, and the Slate-colored and Oregon juncos). Such an intermediate category, however, simply creates two arbitrary boundaries about which to make decisions, whereas we have only one in the present system. Certainly there will be disagreements with many of our decisions, as already evidenced by the qualified ornithologists who have so kindly offered suggestions regarding a preliminary classification. Hopefully these disagreements will be constructively directed toward improving the present classification.

3. The scope of literature coverage was, with few exceptions, limited to material appearing in North American books and journals and dealing with nestings in North America north of Mexico. One major exception to this practice was the treatment of the Winter Wren, which is considered here to be a polygynous species on the basis of studies in Europe. No North American population has yet been investigated adequately, and there is some doubt about its being polygynous on this continent (Verner and Willson, 1966).

While the literature coverage is not a completely exhaustive one, we have endeavored to make it that within the limitations of the library resources we had available. The libraries of the University of California at Berkeley, Harvard University, the University of Illinois, and the University of Washington were combed. We have been unable to fill in some gaps, particularly in a few of the regional journals with restricted distribution. In general, we did not push the coverage back earlier than 1880.

4. Our chief interest was in recording any behavior that takes the male's time from advertising for additional mates during the nest-building, incuba-

tion, nestling, or fledgling periods. A major difficulty here resulted from ambiguous reporting that necessitated several rules in interpreting reports. First, reports that a "pair" was building a nest or that "parents" were feeding young were never taken to mean that the male was actually participating. It was necessary to follow this procedure because some observers reported a "pair" building a nest and in a later sentence stated that the male took no part in nest construction!

Second, it was impossible to assume that the male did not incubate and care for the young simply because an observer indicated that the female did so. It is essential to indicate that *only* the female incubates or that the male *does not* do so.

Third, students of avian behavior often fail to differentiate between nestlings and fledglings. If an author referred only to a male feeding *young*, we assumed he meant nestlings unless we could determine otherwise from the text.

Equal weight was given to each author's comments, even though some observers based their conclusions on larger samples of males than did others. This convention was chosen as an expediency, since it was commonly impossible to determine the extent of an observer's experience with the species being described. References were cited but the data not tallied when (1) it was clear that a report was based on a previously cited publication by another author, or (2) the same author had already been cited for that species, and it was clear that no additional observations were being reported. This occasionally resulted in fewer reports being tallied than there were references cited (e.g. the Cactus Wren, Swainson's Thrush, and Bachman's Warbler).

Finally, an additional source of error we could not eliminate is that of the original observer.

RESULTS

All results are presented in Table 1, and special summaries are provided in Tables 2, 3, and 4. A total of 291 species has been considered, and information has been sought on four phases of the nesting cycle. In all, 4318 observations have been logged in four phases as follows: (1) nest construction—1109, (2) incubation—927, and feeding the incubating female—398, (3) nestling—1435, and (4) fledgling—449. Of the total of 1164 data blocks in Table 1, 793 (68 percent) have data entered. There are 38 species (13 percent of species considered) for which no data were found. Entries were made in only one data block for 27 species (10 percent), in two blocks for 40 species (14 percent), in three blocks for 58 species (19 percent), and in all four blocks for 128 species (44 percent). These results suggest a surprisingly inadequate coverage of the breeding biology of North American passerine birds in general.

KEY TO TABLE 1

MATING SYSTEM:

Mg = normally monogamous
Py = normally polygynous (at least 5 percent of males with two or more mates simultaneously)
(Py) = polygyny reported but apparently abnormal
(Pn) = polyandry reported but apparently abnormal
Pr = promiscuous (no lasting pair-bond; copulation by both sexes likely to involve more than one member of the other).

No designation is provided for most species, indicating that no specific reference to mating system was located in the literature searched. We believe most of these species to be normally monogamous and have so treated them in the present analysis.

SEXUAL VARIATION (see text):

Mon = sexually monomorphic
Dim = sexually dimorphic

ROLE OF MALE IN NESTING CYCLE:

Numbers in the center of each data block indicate the number of separate reports that the male *did* behave as indicated. Numbers in italics on the right side of the data blocks indicate the number of reports that the male *did not* perform the behavior (see text for further explanation).

Nest Building:

B = gathers nest materials and/or builds nest
O = occasionally B
R = rarely B
G = guards nest during construction period
A = accompanies gathering and/or building female
OA = occasionally A
RA = rarely A

Incubation:

I = incubates or covers eggs
O = occasionally I
R = rarely I
F ♀ = feeds female, usually as she incubates
OF ♀ = occasionally F ♀
RF ♀ = rarely F ♀

Feed Nestlings or Fledglings:

F = feeds nestlings or fledglings
O = occasionally F
R = rarely F

REFERENCES:

Numbers in reference section correspond to appropriate numbers in the bibliography. Numbers in italics indicate citations that specifically mention mating systems. References 1580–1585 are simply listed in Table 1, but the data are not tabulated in any of the tables.

TABLE 1

SPECIES-BY-SPECIES COMPILATION OF MATING SYSTEMS, THE EXTENT OF SEXUAL VARIATION, AND REPORTS OF THE BEHAVIOR OF MALE NORTH AMERICAN PASSERINE BIRDS IN THE NESTING CYCLE. (SEE KEY ON OPPOSITE PAGE FOR EXPLANATION OF SYMBOLS EMPLOYED.)

Species	Mating System Sexual Variation	Nest Building Period	Incu- bation Period	Nest- ling Period	Fledg- ling Period	References
COTINGIDAE						
Rose-throated Becard (*Platypsaris aglaiae*)	Dim	B 1 O 1 A 2	I 1			181, 344, 731, 1117, 1271
TYRANNIDAE						
Eastern Kingbird (*Tyrannus tyrannus*)	Mon	B 9 *1* A 1	I 3 *2* O 3 G 4			120, 123, 222, 337, 353, 362, 460, 492, 510, 620, 623, 731, 757, 1023, 1045, 1206, 1303, 1404, 1475, 1566, 1581
Gray Kingbird (*Tyrannus dominicensis*)	Mon					
Tropical Kingbird (*Tyrannus melancholi- cus*)	Mon	B *2* A 2	I 1 *2* G 2	F 2	F 1	1267, 1269, 1271

TABLE 1 (Continued)

Species	Mating System Sexual Variation	Nest Building Period	Incubation Period	Nestling Period	Fledgling Period	References
TYRANNIDAE (Continued)						
Thick-billed Kingbird (*Tyrannus crassirostris*)	Mon	B 1	I 2	F 1		825, 1577
Western Kingbird (*Tyrannus verticalis*)	Mon	B 5 A 1	I 2 O 1 G 1	F 2		82, 120, 123, 460, 830, 1421, 1510, 1512
Cassin's Kingbird (*Tyrannus vociferans*)	Mon		I 2	F 1		120, 123, 1512
Scissor-tailed Flycatcher (*Muscivora forficata*)	Mon	B *1* A 1	I 1 *3* G 2	F 5	F 1	120, 123, 451, 522, 731, 835, 1342
Kiskadee Flycatcher (*Pitangus sulphuratus*)	Mon	B 2				263, 1114
Sulphur-bellied Fly- catcher (*Myiodynastes luteiventris*)	Mon	B *1* A 2	I *1* G 1	F 1		123, 731, 1269
Great Crested Flycatcher (*Myiarchus crinitus*)	Mon	B 7 *2* O 2 A 6	I 3 *2* O 1	F 11 *1*	F 3	34, 120, 123, 130, 197, 460, 472, 490, 492, 501, 731, 760, 764, 838, 918, 966, 1045, 1073, 1233, 1328, 1367, 1408, 1504
Wied's Crested Flycatcher (*Myiarchus tyrannulus*)	Mon					
Ash-throated Flycatcher (*Myiarchus cinerascens*)	Mon	B 1 O 1 A 2	I *2* F♀ *1*	F 5	F 1	120, 123, 476, 568, 694, 1512
Olivaceous Flycatcher (*Myiarchus tuberculifer*)	Mon			F 1		123
Nutting's Flycatcher (*Myiarchus nuttingi*)	Mon					
Eastern Phoebe (*Sayornis phoebe*)	(Py) Mon	B 4 *4* O 1 A 3 OA 1	I 3 *6* O 4 G 1 F♀ 3 *2*	F 18 *2*	F 1	120, 123, 229, 272, 273, 307, 329, 375, 427, 460, 492, 563, 611, 686, 731, 745, 757, 847, 871, 956, 1045, 1060, 1070, *1242*, 1286, 1374, 1399, 1475, 1517
Black Phoebe (*Sayornis nigricans*)	Mon	B 2 *2*	I 2 *2*	F 4	F 3	123, 445, 687, 1046, 1269, 1512
Say's Phoebe (*Sayornis saya*)	Mon	B *1*	I *1*	F 3	F 4	120, 123, 452, 560, 1512

TABLE 1 (Continued)

Species	Mating System / Sexual Variation	Nest Building Period	Incubation Period	Nestling Period	Fledgling Period	References
TYRANNIDAE (Continued)						
Yellow-bellied Flycatcher (*Empidonax flaviventris*) Mon		B *1*	I *1*	F 1	F 1	1193, 1469
Acadian Flycatcher (*Empidonax virescens*) Mon		B 1 *1* A 1	I *3* F♀ 2 *2*	F 5 *1*	F 3	179, 492, 841, 973, 996, 1464, 1583
Traill's Flycatcher (*Empidonax traillii*) Mon		B 1 *1*	I *2* G 1	F 4 R 1		123, 289, 507, 757, 858, 1070, 1512
Least Flycatcher (*Empidonax minimus*) Mon		B 2 *3* A 1 *1*	I 4 *5* R 1	F 8	F 1	120, 123, 340, 460, 621, 644, 731, 744, 757, 876, 970, 1022, 1206, 1327
Hammond's Flycatcher (*Empidonax hammondii*) Mon		O 1	I *1*	F 2	F 1	123, 339, 535
Dusky Flycatcher (*Empidonax oberholseri*) Mon		B 2	I *1*			699, 1372
Gray Flycatcher (*Empidonax wrightii*) Mon		B *1* O 1 A 1	I 2	F 1		699, 731, 1200
Western Flycatcher (*Empidonax difficilis*) Mon			I *1* F♀ 2	F 5		123, 343, 429, 821, 987, 1512, 1561
Buff-breasted Flycatcher (*Empidonax fulvifrons*) Mon		B 2	G 1	F 1	F 1	181, 856, 1536
Coues' Flycatcher (*Contopus pertinax*) Mon					F 1	123
Eastern Wood Pewee (*Contopus virens*) Mon		B 1 *3*	I *2* G 1	F 3 O 1	F 1	120, 123, 460, 514, 731, 757, 1307, 1363
Western Wood Pewee (*Contopus sordidulus*) Mon		B 1 *1* A 1	I *1*	F 3		123, 465, 537, 879, 1512
Olive-sided Flycatcher (*Nuttallornis borealis*) Mon			I 1 G 1 F♀ 1	F 1	F 2	123, 197, 285, 450, 598, 1070
Vermilion Flycatcher (*Pyrocephalus rubinus*) Dim		B *1* A 1	I 1 *1* O 1		F 4	120, 123, 181, 1396, 1512
Beardless Flycatcher (*Camptostoma imberbe*) Mon		B *1* A 1		F 1		51, 181

TABLE 1 (Continued)

Species	Mating System / Sexual Variation	Nest Building Period	Incubation Period	Nestling Period	Fledgling Period	References
ALAUDIDAE						
Horned Lark (*Eremophila alpestris*)	Mon	B 1 *2*	I 3 *8* O 1 F♀ 2 *1* RF♀ 1	F 24	F 6	27, 71, 120, 123, 163, 274, 320, 322, 391, 393, 460, 506, 604, 725, 731, 757, 822, 849, 957, 1070, 1085, 1115, 1121, 1229, 1253, 1345, 1347, 1355, 1376, 1431, 1512
HIRUNDINIDAE						
Violet-green Swallow (*Tachycineta thalassina*)	(Py) Mon		I 1 *1* F 1	F 2 O 1		*123*, 291, 726
Tree Swallow (*Iridoprocne bicolor*)	(Py) Mon	B 7 *1* R 1	I 7 *1* R 2 G 2 F♀ 4	F 18 *1*	F 1	215, 232, 255, 267, 268, 269, 461, 541, *626*, 705, 731, 757, 782, 828, 852, 853, 1045, 1070, 1082, 1104, 1194, 1331, 1503, 1507, 1512
Bank Swallow (*Riparia riparia*)	Mon	B 7	I 6	F 7	F 2	32, 123, 134, 461, 474, 491, 731, 757, 1070, 1105, 1330, 1332, 1333
Rough-winged Swallow (*Stelgidopteryx ruficollis*)	Mon	B 2 A 1	I 2 *3* F♀ 1	F 5 *1*	F 2	123, 141, 143, 196, 219, 461, 491, 855, 1029, 1269
Barn Swallow (*Hirundo rustica*)	Mg Mon	B 14 *1* R 1	I 15 O 2	F 16	F 4	123, 341, 416, 461, 474, 491, 494, 540, 582, 623, 697, 731, 757, 789, 834, 992, 1032, 1070, 1193, 1282, 1285, 1305, 1499, 1509, 1512, 1553, 1554, *1566*
Cliff Swallow (*Petrochelidon pyrrhonota*)	(Py) Mon	B 13 R 1	I 4 O 1	F 3		87, 123, 213, 311, 312, 417, *418*, 461, 474, 491, 535, 757, 1070, 1232, 1438, 1505
Cave Swallow (*Petrochelidon fulva*)	Mon	B 1				1535
Purple Martin (*Progne subis*)	Mg (Py) Dim	B 10 O 1 A 2	I 8 *2* O 1 G 3 F♀ 3 *1*	F 18	F 1	47, 121, 123, 257, 336, 347, 363, 461, 491, 639, *704*, 731, 751, 757, 854, 890, *991*, 1070, 1072, 1091, *1299*, 1328, 1371, 1399, 1410, 1411, 1490, 1522, 1524, 1538, 1566

Table 1 (Continued)

Species	Mating System — Sexual Variation	Nest Building Period	Incu-bation Period	Nest-ling Period	Fledg-ling Period	References
CORVIDAE						
Gray Jay (*Perisoreus canadensis*)	Mon	B 5	I 1 *3*	F 4 R 1		1, 120, 124, 474, 705, 731, 809, 1070, 1476, 1512
Blue Jay (*Cyanocitta cristata*)	Mon	B 13	I 8 2 F♀ 6	F 9	F 1	120, 124, 383, 460, 492, 572, 731, 757, 806, 828, 1026, 1070, 1187, 1193, 1255, 1278, 1377, 1475, 1566
Steller's Jay (*Cyanocitta stelleri*)	Mg Mon	B 4	I 2 O 1 G 1 F♀ 2	F 2		120, 124, 181, 209, *211*, 474, 932, 1251
Scrub Jay (*Aphelocoma coeru-lescens*)	Mon	B 9 A 1	I 2 *3* F♀ 4	F 5	F 1	48, 120, 124, 210, 404, 526, 528, 537, 572, 694, 731, 830, 912, 1512
Mexican Jay (*Aphelo-coma ultramarina*)	Mon	B 2	I 1 *1* F♀ 1	F 3		181, 210, 545, 572, 731
Green Jay (*Cyanocorax yncas*)	Mon					
Black-billed Magpie (*Pica pica*)	Mg Mon	B 3	I *4* R 1 F♀ 5	F 1		120, 124, 346, 422, 731, *829*, 1250, 1512
Yellow-billed Magpie (*Pica nuttalli*)	Mg Mon	B 2	I *1* F♀ 3	F 2	F 2	120, 124, 731, *829*
Common Raven (*Corvus corax*)	Mg Mon	B 1 O 1 A 1	I 8 O 2 F♀ 3	F 5	F 2	71, *82*, 120, 124, 460, 474, *577*, 705, 731, 757, 784, 980, 1070, 1399, 1424, 1512
White-necked Raven (*Corvus cryptoleucus*)	Mon	B 3 *1* A 2	I 1	F 1		120, 124, 180, 181, 277, 1244
Common Crow (*Corvus brachyrhynchos*)	(Py) Mon	B 4	I 5 2 F♀ 2	F 7		16, 87, 120, *124*, *460*, 492, 509, 702, 731, 757, 1070, *1080*, 1566
Fish Crow (*Corvus ossifragus*)	Mon	B 1	I 3 *1* F♀ 1	F 1		120, 124, 460, 492
Piñon Jay (*Gymno-rhinus cyanocephala*)	Mon	B 2	I 3	F 1		124, 240, 1512
Clark's Nutcracker (*Nucifraga columbiana*)	Mon	B 4	I 6 F♀ 2 *1*	F 4	F 1	120, 124, 176, 377, 696, 705, 731, 906, 907, 1265, 1512

TABLE 1 (Continued)

Species	Mating System / Sexual Variation	Nest Building Period	Incubation Period	Nestling Period	Fledgling Period	References
PARIDAE						
Black-capped Chickadee (*Parus atricapillus*)	Mg (Py) / Mon	B 23	I 6 *2* F♀12	F 24	F 4	20, 124, 152, 185, 186, 226, 234, 282, 307, 348, 367, 444, 445, 452, 459, 461, 462, 518, 705, 731, 757, 784, 828, 840, 951, 1031, *1048*, 1049, 1070, 1142, 1153, 1176, 1189, 1193, 1197, 1212, *1276*, 1313, 1317, 1390, 1391, 1401, 1489
Carolina Chickadee (*Parus carolinensis*)	Mon	B 3 A 1	I 1 *1* F♀ 1	F 1		124, 172, 185, 186, 1050
Mexican Chickadee (*Parus sclateri*)	Mon	B *1* A 1				181
Mountain Chickadee (*Parus gambeli*)	Mon		F♀ 1	F 6		124, 535, 537, 705, 1201, 1208
Gray-headed Chickadee (*Parus cinctus*)	Mon					
Boreal Chickadee (*Parus hudsonicus*)	Mon			F 6		124, 579, 731, 846, 1070, 1112, 1466
Chestnut-backed Chickadee (*Parus rufescens*)	Mon	B *1* A 1				536
Tufted Titmouse (*Parus bicolor*)	Mg / Mon	B 1 *2* A 5	I 1 *1* O 1 F♀ 5	F 8		124, 238, 307, *382*, 407, 574, 682, 731, 805, 1123, 1175, 1220, 1270, 1407, 1482
Black-crested Titmouse (*Parus atricristatus*)	Mon	A 1	I 2 *1* F♀ 1			124, *382*, 1233
Plain Titmouse (*Parus inornatus*)	Mg / Mon	B 2 A 1	I 3 *2*	F 3		5, 82, 124, 381, *1141*, 1512
Bridled Titmouse (*Parus wollweberi*)	Mon		F♀ 1			882
Verdin (*Auriparus flaviceps*)	Mon	B 3	G 1	F 3		124, 731, 1097, 1512, 1534
Common Bushtit (*Psaltriparus minimus*)	Mon	B 9	I 3 *1* F♀ 1	F 7		6, 124, 181, 443, 445, 448, 535, 536, 731, 986, 1063, 1097, 1164, 1512

TABLE 1 (Continued)

Species	Mating System Sexual Variation	Nest Building Period	Incu- bation Period	Nest- ling Period	Fledg- ling Period	References
PARIDAE (Continued)						
Black-eared Bushtit (*Psaltriparus melanotis*)	Dim	B 3	I 4 *1*	F 4		1266, 1269, 1270, 1271
SITTIDAE						
White-breasted Nuthatch (*Sitta carolinensis*)	Mg Mon	B 17 *1* A 1	I 3 G 1 F♀18	F 15	F 3	22, 42, 45, 61, 86, 125, 182, 235, 349, 370, 461, 491, 535, 537, 540, 609, 683, 731, *746*, 757, 784, 873, 931, 1070, 1148, 1182, 1340, 1407, 1437, 1485, *1512, 1521*, 1533, 1546
Red-breasted Nuthatch (*Sitta canadensis*)	Mg Mon	B 12 *1* A 1	I 4 F♀11	F 8	F 1	42, 82, 125, 192, 226, 435, 535, 540, 551, 615, 731, *746*, 747, 748, *757*, 784, 910, 944, 945, 946, 947, 1070, 1126, 1236, 1582
Brown-headed Nuthatch (*Sitta pusilla*)	Mon	B 8	I 2 *1* F♀ 3	F 6	F 1	86, 125, 477, 656, 1040, 1041, 1045, 1054, 1270, 1480
Pigmy Nuthatch (*Sitta pygmaea*)	Mon	B 5	I *1* F♀ 3	F 8	F 2	82, 83, 125, 146, 499, 535, 536, 825, 1040, 1270, 1512
CERTHIIDAE						
Brown Creeper (*Certhia familiaris*)	Mon	B 7 *1* O 1 A 7	I 2 *3* F♀ 5	F 15	F 3	81, 125, 133, 155, 191, 226, 258, 260, 461, 535, 536, 537, 540, 559, 731, 734, 843, 909, 1070, 1094, 1144, 1180, 1193, 1262, 1263, 1423, 1459, 1539, 1545
CHAMAEIDAE						
Wrentit (*Chamaea fasciata*)	Mg Mon	B 3	I 2	F 3	F 1	125, *419*, 731, 995
CINCLIDAE						
Dipper (*Cinclus mexicanus*)	Mon	B 2 *1* O 1	I *3* F♀ 3	F 11	F 4	90, 125, 308, 389, 414, 415, 511, 566, 614, 705, 830, 933, 936, 1319, 1477, 1512

TABLE 1 (Continued)

Species	Mating System Sexual Variation	Nest Building Period	Incubation Period	Nestling Period	Fledgling Period	References
TROGLODYTIDAE						
House Wren (*Troglodytes aedon*)	Py (Pn) Mon	B 27 O 1	I 2 *1* O 1 R 1 F♀ 6	F 30 *3*	F 6	15, 75, 86, *92, 93,* 112, *125,* 213, *218,* 227, 297, *303,* 304, 307, 330, 358, 408, 455, *461,* 489, 491, 518, 537, 563, 591, *608,* 620, 642, 643, 652, 695, 712, *729,* 731, *732,* 757, 857, 859, 861, 865, 885, 905, *917,* 1019, 1045, *1053,* 1070, 1091, 1119, 1188, 1230, 1241, *1242,* 1245, 1375, 1387, 1425, *1433, 1436,* 1454, 1512, *1542*
Brown-throated Wren (*Troglodytes brunneicollis*)	Mon					
Winter Wren (*Troglodytes troglodytes*)	Py Mon	B 8 *1*	I 2 F♀ *1*	F 4 *3*	F 1	*66, 67,* 125, 164, 328, 602, 721, 722, 731, 757, 866, 880, 1062, 1070, 1260, 1270, *1436,* 1496
Bewick's Wren (*Thryomanes bewickii*)	Mg Mon	B 6	I 2 F♀ 4	F 9	F 4	73, 86, 125, 181, 369, 445, 647, 691, 729, 731, 801, 803, 922, 1061, *1386,* 1397, 1539
Carolina Wren (*Thryothorus ludovicianus*)	Mg Mon	B 11 *1*	I 3 *3* F♀ 7 OF♀ 1	F 10	F 6	2, 25, 111, 125, 226, 349, 401, *452, 461,* 508, 521, 635, 703, 731, 743, 803, 804, 807, 941, 1021, 1270, 1346, *1384,* 1407, 1427, 1526
Cactus Wren (*Campylorhynchus brunneicapillum*)	Mg Mon	B 4		F 3	F 1	52, 53, 54, *55,* 56, 125, 181, 636, 1097
Long-billed Marsh Wren (*Telmatodytes palustris*)	Py Mon	B 13	I 2 *3*	F 5 *1*	F 3	125, 199, 349, 461, 497, 637, *715, 729,* 748, 777, 930, 974, 1019, 1038, 1045, 1183, *1226,* 1432, *1433, 1434, 1435, 1436,* 1497, 1512, *1542*

TABLE 1 (Continued)

Species	Mating System / Sexual Variation	Nest Building Period	Incubation Period	Nestling Period	Fledgling Period	References
TROGLODYTIDAE (Continued)						
Short-billed Marsh Wren (*Cistothorus platensis*)	Py(?) / Mon	B 5		F 1 *1* / O 1	F 1 *1*	86, 97, 125, 461, 967, 1070, 1242, 1407, *1436*, 1443
Cañon Wren (*Catherpes mexicanus*)	Mon	B *1*	I *1* / F♀ 1	F 4		82, 1125, 1406, 1505, 1512
Rock Wren (*Salpinctes obsoletus*)	Mon	B 4	I *1* / F♀ 3	F 2	F 1	125, 241, 731, 833, 1087, 1274, 1406
MIMIDAE						
Mockingbird (*Mimus polyglottos*)	Mg (Py) / Mon	B 8 / O 1 / R 1	I 2 / R 1 / G 1 / F♀ 1	F 12	F 12 *1*	7, 41, 91, 94, *125*, 167, 208, 226, 439, 461, *475*, 481, 512, 529, 581, 757, 795, 796, *800*, 872, 989, 1083, 1162, 1186, 1512
Catbird (*Dumetella carolinensis*)	Mon	B 12 / O 1	I 4 *5* / G 1 / F♀ 3 *1* / OF♀ 2	F 16	F 3	86, 103, 125, 132, 138, 226, 338, 352, 461, 469, 491, 619, 620, 623, 731, 757, 871, 952, 1023, 1070, 1091, 1098, 1238, 1242, 1271, 1417, 1519, 1520, 1578
Brown Thrasher (*Toxostoma rufum*)	Mon	B 7	I 9 *1* / F♀ 1	F 8	F 4	125, 307, 420, 461, 468, 491, 731, 757, 1045, 1091, 1240, 1343, 1382, 1383
Long-billed Thrasher (*Toxostoma longirostre*)	Mon					
Bendire's Thrasher (*Toxostoma bendirei*)	Mon			F 1		694
Curve-billed Thrasher (*Toxostoma curvirostre*)	Mg / Mon		I 6	F 4		55, 125, *276*, *278*, 617, *1306*, 1500
California Thrasher (*Toxostoma redivivum*)	Mon	B 3	I 2	F 1	F 3	125, 1207, 1512
Le Conte's Thrasher (*Toxostoma lecontei*)	Mon	B 1	I 2	F 1		125, 534
Crissal Thrasher (*Toxostoma dorsale*)	Mon		I 3	F 1		125, 894, 1430
Sage Thrasher (*Oreoscoptes montanus*)	Mon		I 2			125, 1372

TABLE 1 (Continued)

Species	Mating System / Sexual Variation	Nest Building Period	Incubation Period	Nestling Period	Fledgling Period	References
TURDIDAE						
Robin (*Turdus migratorius*)	Mg (Py) / Mon	B 12 *10* / O 4 / R 1 / A 2 *2*	I 4 *9* / O 6 / R 1 / G 5 / F♀ 6 *2* / OF♀ 3 / RF♀ 3	F 46 *1*	F 19	17, 126, 148, 149, 166, 170, 171, 173, 271, 287, 296, 306, 310, 386, 411, *461*, 473, 488, 491, 493, 498, 503, 537, 549, 550, 606, 619, 620, 641, 657, *658*, 705, 713, 716, 724, 731, 740, 749, 757, 818, 837, 860, 863, 874, 878, 904, 932, 939, 1045, 1070, 1076, 1116, 1131, 1138, 1193, 1205, 1217, 1218, 1255, 1323, 1388, 1399, 1422, 1478, 1493, 1559, 1571, *1573*, 1574
Fieldfare (*Turdus pilaris*)	Mon					
Varied Thrush (*Ixoreus naevius*)	Dim	B 2 / A 2	I 2			126, 474, 532, 533
Wood Thrush (*Hylocichla mustelina*)	Mg / Mon	B 2 *1* / R 1 / A 2	I 3 *4* / G 2 / F♀ 1 *1*	F 11	F 7	126, 168, *175*, 214, 246, 307, 491, 569, 701, 706, 731, 988, 1070, 1399, 1487, 1508
Hermit Thrush (*Hylocichla guttata*)	Mon	B 1	I 3 *1*	F 13 / O 1		126, 247, 461, 667, 705, 731, 767, 862, 1103, 1113, 1193, 1212, 1329, 1370, 1392, 1399
Swainson's Thrush (*Hylocichla ustulata*)	Mon			F 2		126, 731, 1314
Gray-cheeked Thrush (*Hylocichla minima*)	Mon	B *1*	I *1* / F♀ *1*	F 2		126, 731, 1472
Veery (*Hylocichla fuscescens*)	Mon		I 1 *3*	F 5		35, 57, 351, 1028, 1399
Eastern Bluebird (*Sialia sialis*)	Mg(Pn)(Py) / Dim	B 11 *4* / O 3 / A 2 / OA 1	I 9 *2* / O 3 / G 4 / F♀ 7 / OF♀ 1	F 34 *3*	F 18	23, 86, 115, 126, 165, 204, *218*, 307, 388, 445, 447, 457, 461, 491, 542, 562, 580, 588, 603, 620, 663, 664, 718, 727, 731, 757, 797, 798, *802*, 896, 1045, 1069, 1070, 1091,

TABLE 1 (Continued)

Species	Mating System Sexual Variation	Nest Building Period	Incubation Period	Nest-ling Period	Fledg-ling Period	References
TURDIDAE (Continued)						
Eastern Bluebird (Continued)						*1092*, 1108, 1150, 1193, 1195, 1212, 1222, 1270, 1273, 1284, 1373, 1380, 1385, 1399, 1474, *1502*, 1566
Western Bluebird (*Sialia mexicana*)	Dim	B 2 *1*	I 1 F♀ 1	F 4	F 1	83, 126, 482, 535, 536, 748
Mountain Bluebird (*Sialia currucoides*)	Dim	B 3 *2* G 2	I 3 *1* G 1 F♀ 4	F 11	F 4	86, 104, 126, 321, 429, 535, 537, 554, 705, 731, 932, 1135, 1512
Wheatear (*Oenanthe oenanthe*)	Dim	B 1	O 1	F 5	F 1	126, 674, 976, 1027, 1354
Bluethroat (*Luscinia svecica*)	Dim					
Townsend's Solitaire (*Myadestes townsendi*)	Mon		I *1*	F 1	F 1	350, 535, 705
SYLVIIDAE						
Arctic Warbler (*Phylloscopus borealis*)	Mon			F 1		977
Blue-gray Gnatcatcher (*Polioptila caerulea*)	Dim	B 26 *1* A 3	I 9 O 1	F 10	F 4	8, 126, 151, 156, 201, 205, 262, 298, 349, 356, 371, 452, 461, 535, 595, 630, 649, 695, 731, 757, 828, 899, 955, 979, 981, 1009, 1071, 1096, 1097, 1130, 1158, 1185, 1290, 1344, 1398, 1399, 1413, 1430, 1494, 1561
Black-tailed Gnatcatcher (*Polioptila melanura*)	Dim	B 1 *1*	I 5	F 3	F 1	126, 617, 1118, 1248, 1512, 1531, 1562, 1564
Golden-crowned Kinglet (*Regulus satrapa*)	Dim	B 1 *1* O 1 A 5		F 4 *2*		193, 288, 461, 757, 881, 901, 1070, 1193, 1361, 1512
Ruby-crowned Kinglet (*Regulus calendula*)	Dim	B *1* A 1	I *1*	F 9	F 4	64, 126, 474, 579, 597, 631, 673, 705, 738, 757, 942, 1140, 1297, 1412
MOTACILLIDAE						
White Wagtail (*Motacilla alba*)	Mon					

TABLE 1 (Continued)

Species	Mating System Sexual Variation	Nest Building Period	Incubation Period	Nestling Period	Fledgling Period	References
MOTACILLIDAE (Continued)						
Yellow Wagtail (*Motacilla flava*)	Mon					
Water Pipit (*Anthus spinoletta*)	Mon		I 3 2 F♀ 3	F 5		71, 86, 127, 461, 474, 547, 698, 731, 748, 1122, 1353
Meadow Pipit (*Anthus pratensis*)	Mon		F♀ 1			786
Sprague's Pipit (*Anthus spragueii*)	Mon		F *1*	F 2		127, 583, 731
BOMBYCILLIDAE						
Bohemian Waxwing (*Bombycilla garrula*)	Mon	B 1				68
Cedar Waxwing (*Bombycilla cedrorum*)	Mg Mon	B 18	I 10 *5*	F 16	F 4	24, 68, 127, 226, 325, 373, 458, 461, 491, 546, 619, 620, 705, 731, 757, 816, 819, 836, 851, 1134, 1149, 1155, 1170, 1193, 1209, 1279, 1331, *1512*
PTILOGONATIDAE						
Phainopepla (*Phainopepla nitens*)	Mg Mon	B 14	I 8 O 1	F 5	F 2	68, 82, 127, 424, 478, 617, 666, 731, 898, 982, 983, 984, 1097, 1152, 1239, *1512*, 1513, 1563
LANIIDAE						
Northern Shrike (*Lanius excubitor*)	Mon	B 4	I 2 *1* F♀ 4	F 1		127, 236, 921, 976
Loggerhead Shrike (*Lanius ludovicianus*)	(Py) Mon	B 4	I 2 *3* O 2 F♀ 6	F 7	F 8	89, 127, 365, 400, 461, *524*, 535, 537, 540, 627, 690, 692, 731, 757, 817, 830, 915, 920, 1007, 1070, 1294, 1331, 1512, 1550
VIREONIDAE						
Black-capped Vireo (*Vireo atricapilla*)	Dim	B 4	I 5	F 2	F 1	11, 127, 190, 223, 516, 519, 934, 1580
White-eyed Vireo (*Vireo griseus*)	Mon	B 2	I 3 *1* F♀ 1	F 1	F 1	127, 372, 491, 557, 1211
Hutton's Vireo (*Vireo huttoni*)	Mon	B 7	I 2 *1* F♀ 1	F 6		40, 127, 536, 1426, 1512, 1513, 1528

TABLE 1 (Continued)

Species	Mating System / Sexual Variation	Nest Building Period	Incubation Period	Nestling Period	Fledgling Period	References
VIREONIDAE (Continued)						
Bell's Vireo (*Vireo bellii*)	Mon	B 6 O 1 A 2	I 9	F 10	F 1	100, 127, 181, 395, 616, 731, 971, 1000, 1006, 1017, 1035, 1128, 1379
Gray Vireo (*Vireo vicinior*)	Mon				F 1	1224
Yellow-throated Vireo (*Vireo flavifrons*)	Mon	B 8 *2* A 3	I 11 F♀ 1 OF♀ 1	F 8		86, 127, 281, 335, 349, 461, 491, 502, 515, 590, 670, 887, 888, 1045, 1124, 1350, 1399, 1515
Solitary Vireo (*Vireo solitarius*)	Mon	B 5 *1* O 1 A 1	I 10 *1* O 1 F♀ 2	F 5	F 1	58, 82, 127, 198, 461, 491, 535, 576, 707, 748, 824, 869, 1052, 1070, 1154, 1261, 1505, 1528, 1561
Black-whiskered Vireo (*Vireo altiloquus*)	Mon					
Yellow-green Vireo (*Vireo flavoviridis*)	Mon	A 1		F 1		127
Red-eyed Vireo (*Vireo olivaceus*)	Mon	B 6 *3* A 7	I 9 *5* F♀ 2 *1*	F 15	F 2	31, 127, 275, 295, 335, 349, 461, 491, 502, 620, 622, 623, 731, 757, 813, 1045, 1070, 1093, 1168, 1179, 1193, 1213, 1298, 1321, 1350, 1407, 1416, 1514
Philadelphia Vireo (*Vireo philadelphicus*)	Mon		I 4 O 1	F 2	F 2	85, 127, 194, 461, 540, 680, 731, 823, 1070
Warbling Vireo (*Vireo gilvus*)	Mon	B 5 *1* A 1	I 15 *1* F♀ 1	F 8	F 1	127, 220, 335, 349, 440, 445, 461, 491, 535, 537, 552, 601, 620, 684, 766, 928, 1070, 1101, 1184, 1193, 1202, 1350
PARULIDAE						
Black-and-white Warbler (*Mniotilta varia*)	Dim	B *1* O 2 A *1*	I 2 *1*	F 15	F 4	128, 266, 461, 681, 693, 730, 731, 757, 770, 943, 1045, 1070, 1097, 1159, 1193, 1283, 1310, 1419, 1495
Prothonotary Warbler (*Protonotaria citrea*)	(Py) Dim	B 6 *2* O 1 A 6	I 3 *3* F♀ 7 OF♀ 1	F 20	F 2	10, 14, 25, 59, 101, 114, 128, 137, 189, 226, 248, 266, 284,

Table 1 (Continued)

Species	Mating System / Sexual Variation	Nest Building Period	Incubation Period	Nestling Period	Fledgling Period	References
PARULIDAE (Continued)						
Prothonotary Warbler (Continued)						349, 461, 587, 731, 735, 788, 828, *814*, 845, 870, 908, 937, 1042, 1215, 1234, 1339, 1440, 1448, 1451, *1454*, 1461, 1567
Swainson's Warbler (*Limnothlypis swainsonii*)	Mon		I *1*			794
Worm-eating Warbler (*Helmitheros vermivorus*)	Mon	B 1 A 1	I *1* F♀ 1	F 1	F 1	128, 225, 293, 575
Golden-winged Warbler (*Vermivora chrysoptera*)	Dim	B 1	I *1* OF♀ 1	F 8	F 2	128, 136, 250, 251, 426, 433, 632, 633, 720, 891, 1068, 1243, 1256
Blue-winged Warbler (*Vermivora pinus*)	Dim		I *3* F♀ *1*	F 7	F 3	128, 136, 250, 251, 266, 610, 1067, 1068, 1203, 1246, 1322, 1568
Bachman's Warbler (*Vermivora bachmanii*)	Dim			F 1	F 1	195, 1324, 1483, 1484
Tennessee Warbler (*Vermivora peregrina*)	Mon		I *1*	F 1 *1*		160, 309, 757
Orange-crowned Warbler (*Vermivora celata*)	Mon					
Nashville Warbler (*Vermivora ruficapilla*)	Dim	B 1 O 1 A 1	I 1 *1* R 1 F♀ 4	F 8 *1*	F 3	128, 187, 461, 632, 634, 730, 731, 754, 757, 811, 958, 1070, 1193, 1309, 1551
Virginia's Warbler (*Vermivora virginiae*)	Mon			F 2		77, 128
Colima Warbler (*Vermivora crissalis*)	Mon	B *1*		F 1		142, 1428
Lucy's Warbler (*Vermivora luciae*)	Mon	B *1* OA 2				128, 181, 504
Parula Warbler (*Parula americana*)	(Py) Dim	B 4 *1* O 2 A 2 *1*	I 1 *1* O 2 F♀ 2 *1*	F 8	F 4	86, 128, 293, 326, 357, 413, 436, 461, 491, 520, 650, 708, 731, 938, 959, 960, 1025, 1109, 1111, 1527, *1541*

TABLE 1 (Continued)

Species	Mating System — Sexual Variation	Nest Building Period	Incubation Period	Nestling Period	Fledgling Period	References
PARULIDAE (Continued)						
Olive-backed Warbler (*Parula pitiayumi*)	Dim					
Olive Warbler (*Peucedramus taeniatus*)	Dim	B *1* A 2 OA 1				181, 1143, 1530
Yellow Warbler (*Dendroica petechia*)	Dim	B 4 *3* O 4 A 1	I 4 *4* O 3 F♀ 11	F 16 *1*	F 2	86, 127, 135, 226, 326, 376, 457, 461, 467, 473, 474, 548, 625, 731, 750, 755, 757, 765, 830, 871, 943, 949, 960, 1065, 1070, 1129, 1221, 1287, 1331, 1372, 1415, 1552
Magnolia Warbler (*Dendroica magnolia*)	Mon	B 3	I 1 *1* O 1 F♀ *1*	F 10	F 2	80, 128, 326, 461, 634, 730, 731, 943, 959, 998, 999, 1017, 1070, 1193, 1212, 1312
Cape May Warbler (*Dendroica tigrina*)	Dim	OA 2				153, 900
Black-throated Blue Warbler (*Dendroica caerulescens*)	Dim	B 1 *1* O 1 A 1	OF♀ 1	F 9		128, 239, 570, 571, 634, 730, 731, 959, 1004, 1033, 1465
Myrtle Warbler (*Dendroica coronata*)	Dim	O 3 A 2	O 2 R 2	F 6	F 2	128, 326, 379, 461, 474, 752, 757, 997, 1002, 1070, 1099, 1442
Audubon's Warbler (*Dendroica auduboni*)	Dim	B 1	O 1 R 1	F 3		128, 1097, 1251, 1512
Black-throated Gray Warbler (*Dendroica nigrescens*)	Dim	A 1		F 2 *1*		128, 162, 441, 1097
Townsend's Warbler (*Dendroica townsendi*)	Dim			F 2		1151, 1254
Black-throated Green Warbler (*Dendroica virens*)	Dim	B 4 *2* O 2 A 1	I *2* R 1 F♀ *2*	F 13 *1* O 1	F 8 *1*	3, 128, 231, 280, 292, 326, 359, 457, 461, 646, 731, 757, 1017, 1020, 1070, 1097, 1127, 1160, 1172, 1311, 1315, 1331, 1394, 1486, 1523
Golden-cheeked Warbler (*Dendroica chrysoparia*)	Dim				F 1	1304

TABLE 1 (Continued)

Species	Mating System / Sexual Variation	Nest Building Period	Incubation Period	Nestling Period	Fledgling Period	References
PARULIDAE (Continued)						
Hermit Warbler (*Dendroica occidentalis*)	Dim			F 1		99
Cerulean Warbler (*Dendroica cerulea*)	Dim	B 1 A 1		F 5	F 1	128, 461, 513, 1258, 1300, 1407, 1555
Blackburnian Warbler (*Dendroica fusca*)	Dim	B 2 A 4 RA 1	I 1 O 1 OF♀ 1	F 6	F 1	128, 757, 814, 1051, 1070, 1139, 1264, 1331, 1399
Yellow-throated Warbler (*Dendroica dominica*)	Mon	B 1 3 O 1 A 1	I 2 F♀ 1			128, 202, 650, 1025, 1481
Grace's Warbler (*Dendroica graciae*)	Mon					
Chestnut-sided Warbler (*Dendroica pensylvanica*)	Mon	B 1 1 O 1	I 3 1 O 1 F♀ 2 1	F 16	F 2	4, 128, 212, 226, 242, 368, 461, 495, 730, 731, 757, 763, 778, 811, 820, 897, 924, 959, 1173, 1214
Bay-breasted Warbler (*Dendroica castanea*)	Dim		I 1 F 3	F 7	F 1	128, 154, 326, 461, 731, 757, 895, 1070, 1308
Blackpoll Warbler (*Dendroica striata*)	Dim	B 1	O 1 F♀ 2	F 3	F 2	128, 474, 1070, 1120
Pine Warbler (*Dendroica pinus*)	Dim	B 2 1 A 2	I 3 F♀ 1 1	F 4	F 1 1	128, 203, 313, 634, 868, 914, 978, 1006, 1193, 1288, 1460
Kirtland's Warbler (*Dendroica kirtlandii*)	Mg (Py) Dim	B 4 G 1	I 3 F♀ 2 1	F 5	F 2	128, 200, 266, *889*, 1441, 1556, 1557, 1558
Prairie Warbler (*Dendroica discolor*)	Py Dim	B 1 A 1	I 1 F♀ 2	F 7	F 2	25, 128, 319, 332, 461, 1034, *1036*, 1169, *1436*, 1462
Palm Warbler (*Dendroica palmarum*)	Mon		I 3	F 5		98, 128, 753, 757, 1470
Ovenbird (*Seiurus aurocapillus*)	(Py) (Pn) Mon	B 3 2 A 1	I 4 F♀ 1 RF♀ 1	F 8 1	F 4	128, 305, 405, 461, 491, *564*, *565*, 731, 768, 960, 1008, 1017, 1045, 1320
Northern Waterthrush (*Seiurus noveboracensis*)	(Py) Mon	B 1 1	I 1	F 3	F 2	405, 474, 491
Louisiana Waterthrush (*Seiurus motacilla*)	Mon	B 3	I 2 F♀ 2 RF♀ 1	F 4		128, 230, 245, 266, 405, 406, 491, 730

TABLE 1 (Continued)

Species	Mating System Sexual Variation	Nest Building Period	Incubation Period	Nestling Period	Fledgling Period	References
PARULIDAE (Continued)						
Kentucky Warbler (*Oporornis formosus*)	Dim	B 3 2 A *1*	I 2 F♀ *1*	F 5 R 1	F 2	128, 266, 290, 354, 461, 815, 828, 848, 1498
Connecticut Warbler (*Oporornis agilis*)	Dim			F 3	F 2	128, 739, 1193, 1467
Mourning Warbler (*Oporornis philadelphia*)	Dim		G 1 F♀ 2	F 3	F 1	113, 157, 243, 317, 1181, 1368
MacGillivray's Warbler (*Oporornis tolmiei*)	Dim			F 6	F 3	82, 128, 374, 474, 537, 787, 1086, 1572
Yellowthroat (*Geothlypis trichas*)	(Py) Dim	B 1 *4* O 2 A 1 *1*	I 10 F♀ 3 *1*	F 19	F 6	39, 86, 128, 266, 307, 349, 441, 445, 461, 491, 645, 689, 731, 757, 771, 774, 828, 965, 1095, 1097, 1161, 1174, 1196, 1206, 1235, 1257, *1325*, 1331, *1436*, 1509
Ground-chat (*Chamaethlypis poliocephala*)	Dim					
Yellow-breasted Chat (*Icteria virens*)	Mon	B 3	I 2 F♀ 1	F 8		128, 302, 306, 491, 731, 742, 772, 1089, 1110, 1512
Red-faced Warbler (*Cardellina rubrifrons*)	Mon			F 1	F 1	615, 1118
Hooded Warbler (*Wilsonia citrina*)	Dim	B 1 *1* O 1 A 2	I 3 F♀ 2	F 8	F 2	128, 139, 249, 279, 461, 464, 527, 530, 585, 731, 792, 1047, 1289, 1399
Wilson's Warbler (*Wilsonia pusilla*)	Dim		G 1 F♀ 2	F 5	F 2	128, 536, 586, 776, 1512
Canada Warbler (*Wilsonia canadensis*)	Dim		I *1*	F 3	F 3	14, 128, 244, 586, 781, 1331
American Redstart (*Setophaga ruticilla*)	(Py) Dim	B 3 *8* O 1 A 1	I 2 *7* F♀ 4 *1* RF♀ 1	F 21	F 7 O 1	29, 65, 88, *102*, 103, 128, 226, 266, 349, 403, 437, 461, 473, 491, 684, 705, 719, 723, 730, 731, 756, 757, 762, 850, 864, 959, 1070, 1153, 1167, 1247, 1331, 1341, 1523
Painted Redstart (*Setophaga picta*)	Mon					

TABLE 1 (Continued)

Species	Mating System / Sexual Variation	Nest Building Period	Incubation Period	Nestling Period	Fledgling Period	References
ICTERIDAE						
Bobolink (*Dolichonyx oryzivorus*)	Py Dim	B 2	I 6 G 1	F 8 *1* O 2	F 2	38, 129, 226, 233, 349, 460, 660, 705, 728, 731, *741*, 757, 884, 926, 927, 1070, 1136, 1206, *1436*, 1512, *1542*, *1584*
Eastern Meadowlark (*Sturnella magna*)	Py Mon	B 6 *1* A *1*	I 3 *3* O 1 F♀ 1	F 3	F 3	28, 120, *129*, 226, 421, 460, 491, 731, 757, *793*, 1070, *1266*, *1436*, 1475, *1542*, 1566
Western Meadowlark (*Sturnella neglecta*)	Py Mon	B 2	I 2			120, *428*, *793*, 1193, *1266*, *1436*, 1512, *1542*
Yellow-headed Blackbird (*Xanthocephalus xanthocephalus*)	Py Dim	B 7	I 1 6 G 1 F♀ 2 *1* OF♀ 2	F 5 *1* O 1 R 1	F 2 O 1	49, 120, 129, 266, *430*, *431*, 432, 470, 731, *830*, *994*, 1190, 1193, *1436*, *1468*, 1505, 1512, *1542*
Red-winged Blackbird (*Agelaius phoeniceus*)	Py Dim	B 2 *10*	I *12* R 1 F♀ 1 *1*	F 9 7 O 6 R 2	F 4 *1*	*12*, *36*, 70, 117, 129, 226, 240, *253*, *254*, 307, *316*, *460*, 470, 491, 505, 537, *553*, *618*, 620, 731, 757, 828, *830*, *892*, *993*, 994, 1006, 1030, 1056, *1057*, 1058, *1059*, 1079, *1183*, *1193*, *1210*, 1226, *1266*, *1338*, *1359*, *1433*, *1436*, *1475*, 1512, 1525, *1542*, *1544*, 1547, *1569*
Tricolored Blackbird (*Agelaius tricolor*)	Py Dim	B 2	I 2	F 2 *1*	F 1	537, *785*, 1056, *1057*, 1058, *1059*, *1436*, *1542*
Orchard Oriole (*Icterus spurius*)	Dim	B 3 2 A 1	I 2 *2* F♀ 2			120, 129, 345, 491, 525, 640, 757, 780, 1100, 1193, 1223, 1381, 1575
Black-headed Oriole (*Icterus graduacauda*)	Mon					
Hooded Oriole (*Icterus cucullatus*)	Dim	B 3 2 O 1 A 5	I *1* F♀ 1	F 2	F 1	79, 120, 129, 181, 384, 1114, 1118, 1335, 1357, 1512
Lichtenstein's Oriole (*Icterus gularis*)	Mon					

TABLE 1 (Continued)

Species	Mating System Sexual Variation	Nest Building Period	Incubation Period	Nestling Period	Fledgling Period	References
ICTERIDAE (Continued)						
Scott's Oriole (*Icterus parisorum*)	Dim	B 1	I *1* G 1 F♀ 1	F 3	F 1	129, 1118, 1430, 1512
Baltimore Oriole (*Icterus galbula*)	Dim	B 7 2 O 4 A 7	I 1 *3* O 1 G 1 F♀ 3 *1*	F 12 R 1	F 3	18, 62, 105, 120, 224, 307, 333, 360, 460, 491, 556, 592, 623, 638, 731, 757, 828, 871, 886, 1023, 1070, 1084, 1091, 1096, 1146, 1193, 1198, 1302, 1331, 1399, 1402, 1475, 1512, 1570
Bullock's Oriole (*Icterus bullockii*)	Dim	B 3 *1*	I *1* R 1	F 2	F 1	120, 129, 445, 446, 672, 757, 1512
Rusty Blackbird (*Euphagus carolinus*)	Dim		I 1 *2* F♀ 2	F 3	F 1	120, 129, 460, 731, 733, 1120, 1206
Brewer's Blackbird (*Euphagus cyano-cephalus*)	Py Dim	B 1 A 1	I *1* R 1 RF♀ 1	F 4 *1*	F 3	120, 129, 398, 537, *830*, 972, 1191, *1436*, 1471, 1512, *1540*
Boat-tailed Grackle (*Quiscalus major*)	Pr Dim	B *4*	I 5 O 2 F♀ *1*	F 2 *5*	F *1*	87, 120, *129*, *661*, 731, *867*, 1045, 1096, 1097, *1225*, *1226*, *1227*, 1418, *1436*
Great-tailed Grackle (*Quiscalus mexicanus*)	Pr Dim	B *2* A 1	I 1 *2* F♀ *1*	F 1 *2*	F *1*	87, 120, *1225*, *1226*, *1227*, *1228*, 1268, *1269*, *1436*
Common Grackle (*Quiscalus quiscula*)	Mg Dim	B 6 *1* A 1	I 4 *3* G 2 F♀ 1	F 8	F 1	95, 120, 240, 425, *438*, 473, 491, 496, 659, 757, 903, 1006, 1070, 1106, *1226*, 1475, 1525, 1566
THRAUPIDAE						
Western Tanager (*Piranga ludoviciana*)	Dim		I 1 *1* F♀ 1	F 7	F 1	129, 537, 599, 705, 726, 1107, 1118, 1249, 1512
Scarlet Tanager (*Piranga olivacea*)	Dim	B 2 2 A 1	I 6 F♀ 4 *1* OF♀ 1	F 9	F 2	30, 183, 226, 265, 461, 491, 558, 731, 773, 925, 1091, 1137, 1163, 1193, 1270, 1331, 1409, 1513, 1566
Hepatic Tanager (*Piranga flava*)	Dim			F 1		1430

Table 1 (Continued)

Species	Mating System / Sexual Variation	Nest Building Period	Incu- bation Period	Nest- ling Period	Fledg- ling Period	References
THRAUPIDAE (Continued)						
Summer Tanager (*Piranga rubra*)	Dim	A *1*	F♀ 1	F 2		129, 452, 453, 828
FRINGILLIDAE						
Cardinal (*Richmondena cardinalis*)	Mg Dim	B 6 7 A 6 *1* RA 1	I 2 *9* G 1 F♀ 7 *1* OF♀ 1	F 29	F 32	63, 169, 174, 221, 228, 261, 283, 299, 300, 307, 349, 364, 385, 461, 483, 484, *485*, 486, 487, 491, 517, 529, 589, 593, 624, 675, 731, 736, 757, 761, 799, 828, 837, 839, 919, 940, 953, 954, 1001, 1006, 1037, 1044, 1045, 1055, 1081, 1145, 1193, 1270, 1316, 1318, 1348, 1351, 1429, *1566*, 1576
Pyrrhuloxia (*Pyrrhuloxia sinuata*)	Dim	B *1*		F 1		517, 1118
Rose-breasted Grosbeak (*Pheucticus ludovicianus*)	Dim	B *2* O 2 A 3	I 39 *1* O 1 F♀ 1	F 13 *1*	F 5	13, 25, 43, 87, 159, 226, 237, 256, 270, 307, 334, 349, 361, 396, 421, 457, 461, 471, 491, 541, 542, 651, 677, 678, 709, 711, 714, 731, 757, 759, 764, 935, 950, 956, 961, 1133, 1144, 1177, 1193, 1271, 1272, 1301, 1351, 1358, 1339, 1403, 1479, 1518, 1566, 1585
Black-headed Grosbeak (*Pheucticus melanocephalus*)	Dim	B *1* A 1	I 8 O 1 F♀ *1*	F 6	F 2	25, 60, 87, 442, 445, 537, 600, 731, 748, 1097, 1251, 1271, 1366, 1501
Blue Grosbeak (*Guiraca caerulea*)	Dim	B 1 2	I 1 *1* G 1 F♀ *1*	F 4 2	F 3	69, 106, 607, 783, 916, 1006, 1512
Indigo Bunting (*Passerina cyanea*)	Dim	B 3 *1* A 1	I 1 7 O 2 F♀ 1 *1*	F 5 *3* O 1	F 2	33, 178, 286, 307, 461, 491, 775, 828, 1045, 1070, 1193, 1351, 1399, 1566
Lazuli Bunting (*Passerina amoena*)	Dim	B 1	I 1 *1* G 1	F 2		399, 899, 1512

TABLE 1 (Continued)

Species	Mating System / Sexual Variation	Nest Building Period	Incubation Period	Nestling Period	Fledgling Period	References
FRINGILLIDAE (Continued)						
Varied Bunting (*Passerina versicolor*)	Dim					
Painted Bunting (*Passerina ciris*)	(Py) Dim	B 2 *1*	I *1*	F *1*	F 1	72, 226, *1077, 1078*, 1337
Dickcissel (*Spiza americana*)	Py Dim	B *3* A 1	I 5	F 2 *6*	F *1*	118, 307, 318, 491, 543, 731, 1147, *1436*, 1439, 1548, 1579
Evening Grosbeak (*Hesperiphona vespertina*)	Dim	B 2 A 3	I 2	F 5	F 2	226, 264, 355, 387, 653, 685, 875, 1219, 1362, 1512, 1529
Purple Finch (*Carpodacus purpureus*)	Dim	B 1 O 1 A 1	I 1 *3* R 1 G 1 F♀ 4 OF♀ 1	F 1 O 1	F 3	226, 315, 461, 705, 757, 808, 975, 1070, 1336, 1405, 1491, 1512
Cassin's Finch (*Carpodacus cassinii*)	Dim		F♀ 1		F 1	429, 1090
House Finch (*Carpodacus mexicanus*)	(Py) Dim	B 4 *1* O 2 A 4	I *1* O 1 F♀ 7	F 9	F 2	50, 131, 423, 480, 500, 535, 536, 612, 826, 883, *911*, 1064, 1118, 1334, 1389, 1512
White-collared Seedeater (*Sporophila torqueola*)	Dim					
Pine Grosbeak (*Pinicola enucleator*)	Dim	B 1	I 2 F♀ 3	F 2	F 1	324, 668, 757, 1070, 1157, 1512
Gray-crowned Rosy Finch (*Leucosticte tephrocotis*)	Mon	B 2 A 2	I 1 2 F♀ 2	F 4	F 1	378, 412, 567, 674, 700, 1156, 1237, 1420, 1511
Black Rosy Finch (*Leucosticte atrata*)	Mg Dim	B *1* A 1	I *1*	F 1		466, 923, *1433*
Brown-capped Rosy Finch (*Leucosticte australis*)	Mon					
Hoary Redpoll (*Acanthis hornemanni*)	Dim		I *1*	F 1		737
Common Redpoll (*Acanthis flammea*)	Dim	B *1*	I 1 2 F♀ 1 *1*	F *1* O 1		366, 538, 674
Pine Siskin (*Spinus pinus*)	Mon	B 2 A 8	I *1* F♀ 6	F 6	F 1	44, 322, 449, 461, 474, 531, 536, 578, 731, 808, 842, 948, 1070, 1102, 1178, 1259, 1365, 1488

TABLE 1 (Continued)

Species	Mating System / Sexual Variation	Nest Building Period	Incubation Period	Nestling Period	Fledgling Period	References
FRINGILLIDAE (Continued)						
American Goldfinch (*Spinus tristis*)	Dim	B 2 *2* G 1 A 4	I *5* F♀12	F 22 O 1	F 8	19, 116, 140, 216, 226, 259, 301, 314, 367, 390, 402, 491, 544, 676, 705, 731, 757, 877, 962, 963, 964, 968, 1018, 1045, 1070, 1192, 1266, 1326, 1351, 1445, 1447, 1449, 1512, 1566
Lesser Goldfinch (*Spinus psaltria*)	Dim	B 2	I *1* F♀ 1	F 1	F 1	832, 932
Lawrence's Goldfinch (*Spinus lawrencei*)	Dim	B *1* A 2	I *1* F♀ 2	F 2		731, 831, 832
Red Crossbill (*Loxia curvirostra*)	Dim	B 3 *2* A 5 OA 1	I *4* F♀ 9	F 5	F 5 *1*	78, 184, 188, 327, 409, 596, 613, 654, 688, 731, 757, 812, 825, 902, 1070, 1088, 1291, 1292, 1293, 1340, 1364, 1414, 1512
White-winged Crossbill (*Loxia leucoptera*)	Dim	B 1	F♀ 2		F 1	327, 461, 1070, 1414
Olive Sparrow (*Arremonops rufivirgata*)	Mon					
Green-tailed Towhee (*Chlorura chlorura*)	Mon					
Rufous-sided Towhee (*Pipilo erythrophthalmus*)	Mg Dim	B 1 *3* A 1 *2*	I 1 *5* O 2 F♀ 3 *1* OF♀ 1 RF♀ 2	F 9	F 7	80, 82, 96, 107, 150, 161, 342, 421, 461, 491, 541, 561, *594*, 605, 662, 731, 830, 1039, 1070, 1097, 1270, 1351
Brown Towhee (*Pipilo fuscus*)	Mon		I *1* G 1		F 2	63, 479
Abert's Towhee (*Pipilo aberti*)	Mon		I *1*	F 1		1193
Lark Bunting (*Calamospiza melanocorys*)	(Pn) Dim		I 2	F 1		*122*, 241, 669, 791
Ipswich Sparrow (*Passerculus princeps*)	Mon					
Savannah Sparrow (*Passerculus sandwichensis*)	Mon	B 2	I 3 *1*	F 4	F 1	86, 461, 757, 871, 1351

TABLE 1 (Continued)

Species	Mating System Sexual Variation	Nest Building Period	Incubation Period	Nestling Period	Fledgling Period	References
FRINGILLIDAE (Continued)						
Grasshopper Sparrow (*Ammodramus savannarum*)	Mon		I 2 2	F 3	F 1	158, 461, 731, 1275, 1351, 1453
Baird's Sparrow (*Ammodramus bairdii*)	Mon		I 1	F 1	F 1	252
Le Conte's Sparrow (*Passerherbulus caudacutus*)	Mon		I 1	F 1		731, 1446
Henslow's Sparrow (*Passerherbulus henslowii*)	Mg Mon		I 2	F 2	F 1	671, 731, 1351
Sharp-tailed Sparrow (*Ammospiza caudacuta*)	Pr Mon		I 1 1	F 1 1		1070, 1436, 1565
Seaside Sparrow (*Ammospiza maritima*)	Mg Mon		I 2	F 1		1400, 1436, 1565
Dusky Seaside Sparrow (*Ammospiza nigrescens*)	Mon					
Cape Sable Sparrow (*Ammospiza mirabilis*)	Mon					
Vesper Sparrow (*Pooecetes gramineus*)	Mon	B 1	I 1 / O 1	F 1	F 1	217, 461, 491, 757, 1070, 1103, 1351
Lark Sparrow (*Chondestes grammacus*)	(Py) Mon	B 1	I 1	F 2	F 1	397, 758, 1351, 1549
Rufous-winged Sparrow (*Aimophila carpalis*)	Mon					
Rufous-crowned Sparrow (*Aimophila ruficeps*)	Mon			F 3		985, 1006, 1532
Bachman's Sparrow (*Aimophila aestivalis*)	Mon	A 1		F 3		119, 147, 206, 294, 893
Botteri's Sparrow (*Aimophila botterii*)	Mon					
Cassin's Sparrow (*Aimophila cassinii*)	Mon					
Black-throated Sparrow (*Amphispiza bilineata*)	Mon			F 1		1118
Sage Sparrow (*Amphispiza belli*)	Mon					
White-winged Junco (*Junco aikeni*)	Mon					

TABLE 1 (Continued)

Species	Mating System Sexual Variation	Nest Building Period	Incubation Period	Nestling Period	Fledgling Period	References
FRINGILLIDAE (Continued)						
Slate-colored Junco (*Junco hyemalis*)	Mon	A 2	G 1	F 12	F 5	434, 456, 523, 648, 655, 731, 757, 1043, 1074, 1075, 1212, 1280, 1281, 1369
Oregon Junco (*Junco oreganus*)	Mon	B 2 A 1		F 6	F 1	536, 1270, 1378, 1506, 1512, 1513, 1539
Gray-headed Junco (*Junco caniceps*)	Mon			F 1	F 1	573, 830
Mexican Junco (*Junco phaeonotus*)	Mon					
Tree Sparrow (*Spizella arborea*)	Mon	B 2 A 2	I *3*	F 6	F 2	37, 108, 109, 110, 491, 628, 629, 731, 1458, 1492
Chipping Sparrow (*Spizella passerina*)	(Py) Mon	B 2 *2* O 1 R 1 A 1	I 1 *1* O 1 R 2 F♀ 3 *1*	F 12	F 6	21, 177, 461, 491, 679, 731, 757, 929, 975, 1070, 1129, 1171, 1199, 1351, 1456, *1463*, 1512, 1513, 1560
Clay-colored Sparrow (*Spizella pallida*)	Mon	B *1* A 2	I 1 *1* O 3	F 6		463, 790, 1129, 1450, 1455, 1473
Brewer's Sparrow (*Spizella breweri*)	Mon					
Field Sparrow (*Spizella pusilla*)	Mon	B 2 *2* A 2	I 2 O 1 F♀ 1 *1* OF♀ 1	F 8 *1* O 1	F 4	323, 491, 563, 662, 712, 731, 1070, 1165, 1351, 1444, 1452, 1457, 1516
Black-chinned Sparrow (*Spizella atrogularis*)	Dim					
Harris' Sparrow (*Zonotrichia querula*)	Mon	B *1*	I *1*			1231
White-crowned Sparrow (*Zonotrichia leucophrys*)	(Py) Mon	B *1*	I *1*	F 3	F 1	*144*, 145, 445, 536, 731
Golden-crowned Sparrow (*Zonotrichia atricapilla*)	Mon			F 1		1360
White-throated Sparrow (*Zonotrichia albicollis*)	Mon	B 2	I 1 2	F 5	F 1	436, 461, 757, 810, 1070, 1193, 1296
Fox Sparrow (*Passerella iliaca*)	Mon	B 1 *1*	I 1	F 3 O 1	F 1	454, 535, 827, 879, 1120, 1512
Lincoln's Sparrow (*Melospiza lincolnii*)	Mon					

TABLE 1 (Continued)

Species	Mating System / Sexual Variation	Nest Building Period	Incubation Period	Nestling Period	Fledgling Period	References
FRINGILLIDAE (Continued)						
Swamp Sparrow (*Melospiza georgiana*)	Py / Mon	B 1 *1*	I 2 / F♀ 1	F 3	F 1 / O 1	491, 757, 1351, *1543*
Song Sparrow (*Melospiza melodia*)	Mg(Py) / Mon	B 6 / O 3	I 1 *4* / O 1 / G 3 / F♀ 1 *1*	F 26	F 13	9, 26, 74, 174, 349, 461, 491, 555, 705, 712, 731, 757, 769, 779, 969, 1001, 1003, 1005, 1010, *1011*, 1012, 1013, *1014*, 1015, *1016*, 1017, 1019, 1066, 1070, 1132, 1206, 1216, 1295, 1351, 1393, *1436*, 1512
McCown's Longspur (*Rhynchophanes mccownii*)	Mg / Dim	B *1*	I 3 / G 1 / F♀ 2	F 3	F 1	392, 394, *913*, 1252
Lapland Longspur (*Calcarius lapponicus*)	Dim	B 3 / A 1	I 3 / F♀ *1*	F 2	F 1	207, 391, 539, 1027, 1356
Smith's Longspur (*Calcarius pictus*)	Dim					
Chestnut-collared Longspur (*Calcarius ornatus*)	Dim		I 2 / F♀ *1*	F 3	F 2	76, 584, 665, 731, 1193
Snow Bunting (*Plectrophenax nivalis*)	(Py) / Dim	B 3 / A 1	I 5 / O 1 / F♀ 2	F 6	F 6	226, 380, 391, 410, 412, 491, 1027, 1204, 1353, *1395*
McKay's Bunting (*Plectrophenax hyperboreus*)	Dim					

Certainly no precise criterion can be employed as a measure of the information required to provide a reasonably adequate resumé of a male's role in the nesting cycle. Even within a given species, variability can occur between individuals, within the same individual from season to season, and even consistently between populations—cf. the Long-billed Marsh Wren (Verner, 1964; Kale, 1965). If we assume that a species is reasonably well known when at least five observers have reported on its behavior relative to at least three of the four phases of the breeding cycle, only 48 species (16 percent) meet the criterion (see Table 2), while only 13 species (4 percent) meet the criterion for all four phases (reports of males feeding incubating females have not been counted among the necessary five reports to assess the male's role in incubation). However, it is true that some species that have been extensively studied by a single observer may be well known, at least for a single population.

TABLE 2

BREAKDOWN, BY FAMILIES, OF THE NUMBERS OF SEXUALLY MONOMORPHIC AND DIMORPHIC SPECIES (SEE TEXT FOR EXPLANATION), MATING SYSTEMS (NUMBERS IN PARENTHESES INDICATE SPECIES WITH INDICATED MATING SYSTEM REPORTED BUT APPARENTLY NOT USUAL), AND EXTENT OF OUR KNOWLEDGE OF SPECIES' LIFE HISTORIES (SEE TEXT FOR EXPLANATION).

Family	Sexual Variation		Mating Systems				Extent of Coverage		
	Sexually Monomorphic	Sexually Dimorphic	Monogamous	Polygynous	Polyandrous	Promiscuous	Well Known	Poorly Known	No Data
Cotingidae	0	1	1	0	0	0	0	1	0
Tyrannidae	30	2	32	(1)	0	0	3	26	3
Alaudidae	1	0	1	0	0	0	1	0	0
Hirundinidae	8	0	8	(4)	0	0	4	4	0
Corvidae	14	0	14	(1)	0	0	2	11	1
Paridae	14	0	14	(1)	0	0	1	12	1
Sittidae	4	0	4	0	0	0	0	4	0
Certhiidae	1	0	1	0	0	0	1	0	0
Chamaeidae	1	0	1	0	0	0	0	1	0
Cinclidae	1	0	1	0	0	0	0	1	0
Troglodytidae	10	0	6	4	(1)	0	3	6	1
Mimidae	10	0	10	(1)	0	0	3	6	1
Turdidae	8	6	14	(2)	(1)	0	3	9	2
Sylviidae	1	4	5	0	0	0	1	4	0
Motacillidae	5	0	5	0	0	0	0	3	2
Bombycillidae	2	0	2	0	0	0	1	1	0
Ptilogonatidae	1	0	1	0	0	0	1	0	0
Laniidae	2	0	2	(1)	0	0	1	1	0
Vireonidae	11	1	12	0	0	0	5	6	1
Parulidae	18	36	53	1 (7)	(1)	0	5	44	5
Icteridae	4	14	9	7	0	2	4	12	2
Thraupidae	0	4	4	0	0	0	1	3	0
Fringillidae	44	33	73	2 (7)	(1)	1	9	49	19
TOTALS	190	101	273	14 (25)	0 (4)	3	49	204	38

Table 2 provides a summary, by families, of the numbers of sexually monomorphic and dimorphic species, of mating systems, and of the extent of our knowledge of the roles of males in the nesting cycle. Polygyny is evidently a rare event in many species and may result when a mated male dies and a neighbor expands his territory to include that of the missing male. Such irregular or suspected cases of polygyny are shown in parentheses in Table 2, as are the four reported cases of polyandry.

Table 3 summarizes the roles of males on the basis of the total numbers of positive and negative reports for each behavior, while Table 4 provides information on the same question but is based only on species for which at least five reports have been recorded during any of the four phases of the cycle. It has commonly been regarded that males of sexually dimorphic species participate less in nesting activities than those of monomorphic species, because they lack cryptic coloration and so are more likely to draw attention to the nest. We have argued above that males of polygynous and promiscuous species are less likely to participate in nesting activities, because such participation requires time that could otherwise be devoted to advertis-

TABLE 3

SUMMARY OF REPORTS ON MALE BEHAVIOR DURING THE NESTING CYCLE ACCORDING TO MATING SYSTEM AND EXTENT OF SEXUAL VARIATION. NUMBERS IN THE CENTER COLUMN OF EACH BLOCK INDICATE THE TOTAL NUMBER OF REPORTS THAT MALES DID PERFORM AS INDICATED; NUMBERS IN ITALICS AT THE RIGHT OF EACH BLOCK GIVE THE TOTAL NUMBER OF REPORTS THAT MALES DID NOT BEHAVE AS INDICATED. FOR AN EXPLANATION OF SYMBOLS, SEE THE KEY TO TABLE 1. SEE FOOTNOTE TO TABLE 4 FOR EXPLANATION OF SUPERSCRIPTS.

Mating System	Sexual Variation	Nest Building Period			Incubation Period			Nestling Period			Fledgling Period		
		B	404	*88*	I	275	*190*	F	751	*12*	F	209	*1*
		O	23		O	37		O	5		O	0	
		R	7		R	8		R	2		R	0	
		G	0	*0*	G	34	*0*						
	Mon	A	88	*5*	F♀	179	*19*						
		OA	3		OF♀	8							
		RA	0		RF♀	6							
		Σ	525	*93*	Σ	547	*209*	Σ	758	*12*	Σ	209	*1*
		%	85ᵃ	*15*	%	72	*28*	%	98ᵇ	*2*	%	99+	*1–*
Monog.													
		B	151	*91*	I	132	*126*	F	508	*17*	F	200	*3*
		O	33		O	27		O	5		O	0	
		R	0		R	7		R	2		R	0	
		G	3	*1*	G	19	*0*						
	Dim	A	92	*8*	F♀	131	*22*						
		OA	5		OF♀	9							
		RA	2		RF♀	3							
		Σ	286	*100*	Σ	328	*148*	Σ	515	*17*	Σ	200	*3*
		%	74ᵃ·ᶜ	*26*	%	69ᵈ	*31*	%	97ᵉ	*3*	%	98ʰ	*2*
		B	62	*3*	I	10	*11*	F	47	*9*	F	15	*1*
		O	1		O	2		O	1		O	1	
		R	0		R	1		R	0		R	0	
		G	0	*0*	G	0	*0*						
	Mon	A	0	*1*	F♀	8	*1*						
		OA	0		OF♀	0							
		RA	0		RF♀	0							
		Σ	63	*4*	Σ	21	*12*	Σ	48	*9*	Σ	16	*1*
Polyg. or Promisc.		%	94ᶠ	*6*	%	64ᵍ	*36*	%	84ᵇ	*16*	%	94	*6*
		B	4	*30*	I	3	*39*	F	40	*24*	F	14	*4*
		O	0		O	2		O	9		O	1	
		R	0		R	2		R	3		R	0	
		G	0	*0*	G	2	*0*						
	Dim	A	4	*0*	F♀	5	*4*						
		OA	0		OF♀	2							
		RA	0		RF♀	1							
		Σ	8	*30*	Σ	17	*43*	Σ	52	*24*	Σ	15	*4*
		%	21ᶜ·ᶠ	*79*	%	28ᵈ·ᵍ	*72*	%	68ᵉ	*32*	%	79ʰ	*21*

ing for additional mates. On the basis of the summaries provided in Tables 3 and 4, the validity of these two generalizations can be examined. Differences between monomorphic/dimorphic and monogamous/polygamous species were tested using the Fisher exact probability test or a χ^2 test, as appropriate; significant differences (5 percent) are indicated in the following discussion by asterisks.

The data strongly suggest that males of a majority of monogamous species assist with nest construction and that, of these, males of monomorphic

TABLE 4

SUMMARY OF THE ROLES OF MALE PASSERINES IN THE NESTING CYCLE ACCORDING TO MATING SYSTEMS AND EXTENT OF SEXUAL VARIATION. NUMBERS INDICATE THE TOTAL SPECIES IN EACH CATEGORY FOR WHICH AT LEAST FIVE REPORTS WERE AVAILABLE FOR THE BEHAVIOR INDICATED. NUMBERS AT THE LEFT OF EACH BLOCK INDICATE THE TOTAL SPECIES FOR WHICH AT LEAST HALF THE REPORTS INDICATE THAT MALES DO BEHAVE AS INDICATED. NUMBERS IN ITALICS, TO THE RIGHT, GIVE THE NUMBER OF SPECIES WHICH DO NOT BEHAVE AS INDICATED, AS JUDGED BY THE MAJORITY OF REPORTS.*

Mating System	Sexual Variation		Build and/or Accompany Building Female		Incubate or Cover Eggs		Feed Incubating Female		Feed Nestlings		Feed Fledglings	
			Yes	No	Yes	No	Yes	No	Yes	No	Yes	No
Monogamous	Monomorphic	Number	44	3	30	8	12	0	63	0	9	0
		Percent	94	6	79	21	100	0	100	0	100	0
	Dimorphic	Number	23	4	11	9	11	1	42	0	10	0
		Percent	85	15	55[c]	45	92	8	100[d]	0	100	0
	TOTAL	Number	67	7	41	17	23	1	105	0	19	0
		Percent	91	9	71[e]	29	96	4	100[f]	0	100	0
Polygynous or Promiscuous	Monomorphic	Number	5	0	2	1	1	0	3	0	1	0
		Percent	100[a]	0	67	33	100	0	100[b]	0	100	0
	Dimorphic	Number	0	2	0	5	2	0	5	2	1	0
		Percent	0[a]	100	0[c]	100	100	0	71[b,d]	29	100	0
	TOTAL	Number	5	2	2	6	2	0	8	2	2	0
		Percent	71	29	25[e]	75	100	0	80[f]	20	100	0

* Statistically significant differences (at the 5 percent level), using χ^2 and Fisher exact probability tests, are indicated in the table by paired superscripts: a, a; b; etc. Monomorphic and dimorphic species (totals) are significantly different during incubation but not during nest-building or feeding of offspring.

species more commonly assist than do those of dimorphic species (85 vs. 74*
percent in Table 3; 94 vs. 85 percent in Table 4). Males of polygynous and
promiscuous species participate somewhat less frequently in nest construction than do males of monogamous species although the difference is wholly
attributable to the near absence of participation by males of the sexually
dimorphic species. Table 3 indicates that among the polygynous species
males of 94 percent of the monomorphic species are involved in nest
construction while males of only 21* percent of the dimorphic species are
so involved; Table 4 indicates an even greater difference (100 vs. 0* percent).
In this connection it is pertinent to note that in four (all wrens) of the
five polygynous species in which males reportedly build nests, the males
make use of several nests as courting sites in the attraction of mates. It is
also noteworthy that all four of these species are sexually monomorphic.

Incubation by males is apparently less common among dimorphic and
polygynous or promiscuous species than among monomorphic and monogamous ones. Again, great contrast is observed between males of monomorphic
and dimorphic species in the polygynous-promiscuous group (64 vs. 28*
percent in Table 3; 67 vs. 0 percent in Table 4), and an additional statistically significant difference lies between dimorphic monogomous and
polygynous males (69 vs. 17* percent in Table 3; 55 vs. 0* percent in
Table 4). Bailey (1952) reported that no male passerine was known to
develop a brood patch, which implies that none incubates. Simply covering
the eggs, however, can significantly reduce their heat loss and thus help in
their development. Moreover, covering the eggs has the same effect on a
male's time budget as has incubation, so the two behaviors are equally
significant in terms of polygyny and promiscuity. While it is usually impossible to determine from published reports whether a male was simply
covering the eggs or was actually applying heat to them, there is evidence
that at least in some passerine species the male truly incubates the eggs.
Incubation patches on male passerines have been reported for the following
species: Great Crested Flycatcher (Parkes, 1953), Barn Swallow (Davis, 1937),
Clark Nutcracker (Mewaldt, 1952), Black-crested Titmouse (Sennett, 1879),
White-bellied Wren (Sutton, 1948), Curve-billed Thrasher (Weston, 1952),
Swainson Thrush (Johnstone, 1949), Western Tanager (Johnstone, 1949),
and Gray-crowned Rosy Finch (Irving, 1960). For six of these species, obser-
vational data support the view that males incubate; for the Western Tanager
the reports are equally divided; and for the Gray-crowned Rosy Finch two
of three reports indicate that the male does not incubate.

In most species adequately reported the male feeds the incubating female.
Little significance can be assigned to this result, however, since very few
observers have reported their failure to observe this behavior. Moreover, it
is important to report at what stage during incubation the feeding occurred,
since it may simply represent early development of parental care behavior
(see Nolan, 1963).

Apparently with rare exceptions male passerines feed their nestlings at
least part of the time. The only two exceptions among 115 species that are
adequately known (Table 4) are both dimorphic and one is polygynous
(Dickcissel) and the other promiscuous (Boat-tailed Grackle). These two
exceptions, however, produce differences between monomorphic and dimorphic polygynous species (100 vs. 71* percent in Table 4) and between

monogamous and polygynous dimorphic species (100 vs. 71* percent in Table 4). Even among some of the other polygynous species (e.g. the Red-winged Blackbird) in which a majority of observers report males feeding nestlings, this behavior is evidently uncommon and possibly confined to the last few days of the nestling period. In such species a premium is placed upon continued advertisement for mates to an extent that it is selectively disadvantageous to devote time to feeding young. However, as the season nears an end, the probability of a male's attracting a new mate and rearing another brood approaches zero, so selection should favor those males that shift their attention to care for any of their young still requiring it.

Basically the same relations seem to apply to the fledgling period as apply to the nestling period, although the number of species adequately reported is woefully small.

DISCUSSION

Tentatively, we interpret the above results to confirm the widely accepted view that males of sexually dimorphic species less frequently participate in nesting activities than do males of sexually monomorphic species. The difference may, in fact, be greater than the data suggest (1) because of the general failure of observers to report things they did not see and (2) because males of sexually monomorphic species may frequently be identified as females so their participation in nesting activities is not as readily recognized as in the case of males of sexually dimorphic species. A greater difference in behavior is indicated between males of monogamous and polygynous or promiscuous species, particularly, in the cases of the latter two mating systems, with males of species that are also sexually dimorphic. The magnitude of the difference in behavior of males in this category and those of all other categories suggests that the effects of natural selection against conspicuously plumed males that frequent the nest site and against males of polygynous or promiscuous species that divert time from mate-attraction behavior to participate in nesting activities have a significant *combined* effect in reducing male participation at the nest.

The general inadequacy of our total knowledge of the life histories of passerine birds pointed up by this review, coupled with the all-too-often sloppy reporting of same, call for a more serious and systematic approach to these natural history studies. It will ultimately be essential for all aspects of the life histories of all species to be expressed in quantitative terms, which will permit analysis of individual and populational variability. Until we know what percentages of what members of what populations perform what behaviors how frequently and at what points in their lives, we cannot hope to generalize accurately about the difference of roles between males of monomorphic and dimorphic species and between males of monogamous and polygynous species.

BIBLIOGRAPHY

1. A., A. W. 1884. The Oregon jay, (*Perisoreus obscurus*). Ornith. and Ool., 9: 69.
2. ABBOTT, C. C. 1884. The Carolina wren; a year of its life. Am. Nat., 18: 21–25.
3. ABBOTT, C. G. 1909a. The black-throated green warbler as a nesting species on Long Island, N. Y. Auk, 26: 80–81.
4. ———. 1909b. A cowbird's nursery. Bird-Lore, 11: 149–153.
5. ADAMS, E. 1898. Notes on the plain titmouse. Osprey, 2: 81–82.
6. ADDICOTT, A. B. 1938. Behavior of the bush-tit in the breeding season. Condor, 40: 49–63.
7. ADKISSON, C. S. 1966. The nesting and behavior of mockingbirds in northern lower Michigan. Jack-Pine Warb., 44: 102–116.
8. ALER, L. M. 1942. Blue-gray gnatcatchers in a Minneapolis public park. Flicker, 14: 23–24.
9. ALFORD, J. P., AND C. L. SHILLIDAY. 1909. Song sparrow. Wils. Bull., 21: 44–45.
10. ALLEN, A. A. 1911. A note on the prothonotary warbler. Auk, 28: 115.
11. ———. 1913. An opportunity interrupted. Bird-Lore, 15: 296–300.
12. ———. 1914. The red-winged blackbird: A study in the ecology of a cattail marsh. Proc. Linn. Soc. N.Y. (Abstr.), 24–25: 43–128.
13. ———. 1918. Photograph of male rose-breasted grosbeak. Bird-Lore, 20: 321.
14. ———. 1919. The warblers of central New York (concluded). Bird-Lore, 21: 149–156.
15. ———. 1927. Jenny Wren's diary. Bird-Lore, 29: 290–301.
16. ———. 1928a. The autobiography of Jim Crow. Bird-Lore, 30: 73–83.
17. ———. 1928b. Cock Robin—his story. Bird-Lore, 30: 142–152.
18. ———. 1928c. Dame Oriole's story. Bird-Lore, 30: 214–222.
19. ———. 1928d. Mother Goldfinch tells her story. Bird-Lore, 30: 287–293.
20. ———. 1929a. Chickadee. Bird-Lore, 31: 69–78.
21. ———. 1929b. The friendly chippy. Bird-Lore, 31: 138–147.
22. ———. 1929c. Nuthatch. Bird-Lore, 31: 423–432.
23. ———. 1930a. Gentle bluebird's story. Bird-Lore, 32: 151–159.
24. ———. 1930b. Cherry bird—the cedar waxwing. Bird-Lore, 32: 298–307.
25. ———. 1930c. The book of bird life. Van Nostrand Co., Inc., Princeton, Toronto, London, New York. 396 pp.
26. ———. 1931a. The song sparrow's story. Bird-Lore, 33: 211–219.
27. ———. 1931b. The prairie horned lark. Bird-Lore, 33: 425–434.
28. ———. 1932a. The meadowlark. Bird-Lore, 34: 85–95.
29. ———. 1932b. The American redstart. Bird-Lore, 34: 222–231.
30. ———. 1932c. The tanager's story. Bird-Lore, 34: 287–295.
31. ———. 1932d. The red-eyed vireo's family story. Bird-Lore, 34: 353–361.
32. ———. 1933a. The bank swallow's story. Bird-Lore, 35: 116–125.
33. ———. 1933b. The indigo bunting. Bird-Lore, 35: 227–235.
34. ———. 1933c. The crested flycatcher's story. Bird-Lore, 35: 285–293.
35. ———. 1934a. The veery and some of his family. Bird-Lore, 36: 68–78.
36. ———. 1934b. The red-wing. Bird-Lore, 36: 128–138.
37. ———. 1934c. The tree sparrow. Bird-Lore, 36: 385–392.
38. ———. 1963a. Photograph of male bobolink. The Living Bird, 2: 100.
39. ———. 1963b. Photograph of male yellowthroat. The Living Bird, 2: 113.
40. ALLEN, A. S. 1930. The construction of a Hutton vireo's nest. Condor, 32: 240–241.
41. ALLEN, F. H. 1910. The mockingbird near Boston. Auk, 27: 460–461.
42. ———. 1912. The white-breasted and red-breasted nuthatches. Bird-Lore, 14: 316–319.
43. ———. 1916. A nesting of the rose-breasted grosbeak. Auk, 33: 53–56.
44. ALLEN, J. A. 1887. The pine finch (*Spinus pinus*) breeding at Cornwall-on-Hudson, N. Y. Auk, 4: 284–286.
45. ALLEN, L. E. 1924. A few nuthatch notes. Ool., 41: 126–128.
46. ———. 1925. Nuthatch nests in central Iowa. Ool., 42: 164–165.
47. ALLEN, R. W., AND M. M. NICE. 1952. A study of the breeding biology of the purple martin (*Progne subis*). Am. Mid. Nat., 47: 606–665.
48. AMADON, D. 1944. Results of the Archbold Expeditions. No. 50. A preliminary life history study of the Florida jay, *Cyanocitta c. coerulescens*. Am. Mus. Novit., 1252: 1–22.

49. AMMANN, G. A. 1938. The life history and distribution of the yellow-headed black-bird. Ph.D. dissertation, library, Univ. of Mich., Ann Arbor.
50. ANDERSON, A. H., AND A. ANDERSON. 1944. 'Courtship' feeding by the house finch. Auk, 61: 477–478.
51. ———. 1948. Notes on two nests of the beardless flycatcher near Tucson, Arizona. Condor, 50: 163–164.
52. ———. 1959. Life history of the cactus wren. Pt. II. The beginning of nesting. Condor, 61: 186–205.
53. ———. 1960. Life history of the cactus wren. Pt. III. The nesting cycle. Condor, 62: 351–369.
54. ———. 1962. Life history of the cactus wren. Pt. V. Fledging to independence. Condor, 64: 199–212.
55. ———. 1963. Life history of the cactus wren. Pt. VI. Competition and survival. Condor, 65: 29–43.
56. ———. 1965. The cactus wrens on the Santa Rita Experimental Range, Arizona. Condor, 67: 344–351.
57. ANNAN, O. 1961. Observations on breeding behavior of veeries in Michigan. Jack-Pine Warb., 39: 62–71.
58. ANONYMOUS. 1895. Report on the vircos. Nidol., 2: 96–97.
59. ANONYMOUS. 1909. The prothonotary warbler. Ool., 26: 102–105.
60. ANONYMOUS. 1938. A nesting season in Scott Valley, Siskiyou Co., Calif. Ool., 55: 53–56.
61. ANTES, F. T. 1903. A nuthatch's nest. Bird-Lore, 5: 196.
62. ———. 1904. Two years for an oriole's nest. Bird-Lore, 6: 134.
63. ANTEVS, A. 1947. Towhee helps cardinals feed their fledglings. Condor, 49: 209.
64. ANTHONY, A. W. 1895. Nesting of the ruby-crowned kinglet in southern California. Nidol., 3: 16–17.
65. APPLEBERRY, E. L. 1959. Redstart nesting at Fayetteville, N. C. Chat, 23: 89.
66. ARMSTRONG, E. A. 1952. Help wanted! Aud. Mag., 54: 164–168.
67. ———. 1955. The wren. Collins, London. 312 pp.
68. ARVEY, M. D. 1951. Phylogeny of the waxwings and allied birds. Univ. of Kansas Pub. Mus. Nat. Hist., 3: 473–530.
69. ATKINSON, K. 1892. The blue grosbeak. Ool., 9: 9–10.
70. ATKINSON, W. L. 1900. Our western blackbirds. Ool., 17: 74–76.
71. AUSTIN, O. L., JR. 1932. The birds of Newfoundland Labrador. Mem. Nuttall Ornith. Club, 7: 1–229.
72. B., A. B. 1892. Some of our Louisiana birds. Ool., 9: 138–140.
73. B., H. B. 1892. The genus *Thryothorus*. Ool., 9: 225–227.
74. BAASCH, K. W. 1927. A permanent resident song sparrow. Bull. N.E. Bird-Banding Assoc., 3: 19.
75. BABBITT, C. H. 1952. Christopher Wren and the eternal triangle. Bull. Mass. Aud. Soc., 36: 258–259.
76. BAILEY, A. M., AND R. J. NIEDRACH. 1938. The chestnut-collared longspur in Colorado. Wils. Bull., 50: 243–246.
77. ———. 1938. Nesting of Virginia's warbler. Auk, 55: 176–178.
78. BAILEY, A. M., R. J. NIEDRACH, AND A. L. BAILEY. 1953. The red crossbills of Colorado. Museum Pictorial No. 9. Denver Mus. Nat. Hist. 63 pp.
79. BAILEY, F. M. 1910. The palm-leaf oriole. Auk, 27: 33–35.
80. ———. 1912. Birds of the cottonwood groves. Condor, 14: 113–116.
81. ———. 1916. A home in the forest. Bird-Lore, 18: 229–233.
82. ———. 1928. Birds of New Mexico. Judd and Detweiler, Inc., Washington, D. C. 807 pp.
83. ———. 1939. Among the birds in the Grand Canyon country. U. S. Gov't Printing Office, Washington, D. C. 211 pp.
84. BAILEY, R. E. 1952. The incubation patch of passerine birds. Condor, 54: 121–136.
85. BAILLIE, J. L., JR., AND C. E. HOPE. 1947. The summer birds of Sudbury District, Ontario. Contr. Royal Ont. Mus. Zool., 28: 1–32.
86. BAIRD, S. F., T. M. BREWER, AND R. RIDGWAY. 1874a. A history of North American birds. Land birds, vol. 1. Little, Brown, and Co., Boston. 596 pp.
87. ———. 1874b. A history of North American Birds. Land birds, vol. 2. Little, Brown, and Co., Boston. 590 pp.
88. BAKER, B. W. 1944. Nesting of the American redstart. Wils. Bull., 56: 83–90.

89. BAKER, B., AND E. BAKER. 1952. Loggerhead shrike with malformed bill. Wils. Bull., 64: 161.

90. BAKUS, G. J. 1959. Observations on the life history of the dipper in Montana. Auk, 76: 190–207.

91. BALDWIN, MRS. L. G. 1901. Mockingbird notes. Bird-Lore, 3: 192–193.

92. BALDWIN, S. P. 1921. The marriage relations of the house wren (*Troglodytes a. aedon*). Auk, 38: 237–244.

93. BALDWIN, S. P., AND S. C. KENDEIGH. 1927. Attentiveness and inattentiveness in the nesting behavior of the house wren. Auk, 44: 206–216.

94. BALLOWE, H. L. 1895. The mockingbird. Ool., 12: 163–164.

95. BANKS, J. W. 1885. Nest and eggs of the rusty grackle (*Scolecophagus ferrugineus*). Auk, 2: 106–107.

96. BARBOUR, R. W. 1951. Observations on the breeding habits of the red-eyed towhee. Am. Mid. Nat., 45: 672–678.

97. BARKER, B. W. 1932. Mock nest of short-billed marsh wren. Ool., 49: 92.

98. ———. 1945. A nest of the yellow palm warbler in the Bangor Bog. Bull. Maine Aud. Soc., 1: 42.

99. BARLOW, C. 1899. Nesting of the hermit warbler in the Sierra Nevada Mountains, California. Auk, 16: 156–161.

100. BARLOW, J. C. 1962. Natural history of the Bell vireo *Vireo bellii* Audubon. Univ. of Kansas Pub. Mus. Nat. Hist., 12: 241–296.

101. BARNES, R. M. 1889. Nesting of the prothonotary warbler. Ornith. and Ool., 14: 37–38.

102. BARNEY, C. C. 1929. Redstart neighbors. Bull. Mass. Aud. Soc., 15: 10.

103. ———. 1945. Watching the birds build. Bull. Mass. Aud. Soc., 29: 211–212.

104. BARTLETT, W. A. 1941. Taming bluebirds. Ool., 58: 142–144.

105. BASKETT, J. N. 1900. Sanitary habits of birds. Auk, 17: 299–300.

106. BASSETT, O. 1956. A summer with blue grosbeaks. Nebraska Bird Review, 24: 5–6.

107. BAUMANN, S. A. 1959. The breeding cycle of the rufous-sided towhee, *Pipilo erythrophthalmus* (Linnaeus), in central California. Wasmann Jour. Biol., 17: 161–220.

108. BAUMGARTNER, A. M. 1937a. Food and feeding habits of the tree sparrow. Wils. Bull., 49: 65–80.

109. ———. 1937b. Nesting habits of the tree sparrow at Churchill, Manitoba. Bird-Banding, 8: 99–108.

110. ———. 1938. A study of development of young tree sparrows at Churchill, Manitoba. Bird-Banding, 9: 69–79.

111. BAYNARD, O. E. 1909. Nesting of Florida wren. Ool., 26: 213–215.

112. BAYLISS, C. K. 1917. A remarkable case of bird-feeding. Auk, 34: 90–91.

113. BEAL, C. M. 1927. The mourner of the slashings. Bird-Lore, 29: 255–256.

114. BEARDSLEE, C. S., AND H. D. MITCHELL. 1965. Birds of Niagara Frontier Region. Buffalo Soc. Nat. Sci., 22: 1–478.

115. BECKER, MRS. P. A. 1944. One season of bluebirds. Flicker, 16: 62–64.

116. BEEBE, R. H. 1905. A goldfinch study. Bird-Lore, 7: 189–191.

117. BEER, J. R., AND D. TIBBITS. 1950. Nesting behavior of the red-wing blackbird. Flicker, 22: 61–77.

118. BELLROSE, F. 1936. Late nesting records for northern Illinois. Auk, 53: 348.

119. BENDIRE, C. E. 1888. Notes on the nest and eggs of *Peucaea aestivalis bachmani* Aud., Bachman's sparrow. Auk, 5: 351–356.

120. ———. 1895. Life histories of North American birds. U. S. Nat. Mus. Special Bull., 3: 1–518.

121. BENT, A. A. 1932. More about the purple martins. Bull. Mass. Aud. Soc., 16 (6): 7–9.

122. BENT, A. C. 1908. Summer birds of southwestern Saskatchewan. Auk, 25: 25–35.

123. ———. 1942. Life histories of North American flycatchers, larks, swallows, and their allies. U. S. Nat. Mus. Bull., 179: 1–555.

124. ———. 1946. Life histories of North American jays, crows, and titmice. U. S. Nat. Mus. Bull., 191: 1–495.

125. ———. 1948. Life histories of North American nuthatches, wrens, thrashers, and their allies. U. S. Nat. Mus. Bull., 195: 1–435.

126. ———. 1949. Life histories of North American thrushes, kinglets, and their allies. U. S. Nat. Mus. Bull., 196: 1–454.

127. ———. 1950. Life histories of North American wagtails, shrikes, vireos, and their allies. U. S. Nat. Mus. Bull., 197: 1–411.

128. ———. 1953. Life histories of North American wood warblers. U. S. Nat. Mus. Bull., 203: 1–734.

129. ———. 1958. Life histories of North American blackbirds, orioles, tanagers, and allies. U. S. Nat. Mus. Bull., 211: 1–459.

130. BERGER, A. J. 1966. The nestling period of the great crested flycatcher. Wils. Bull., 78: 320.

131. BERGTOLD, W. H. 1913. A study of the house finch. Auk, 30: 40–73.

132. BERRY, K. F. 1948. A spring caller. Bull. Mass. Aud. Soc., 32: 183–186.

133. BETTS, N. de W. 1909. Brown creepers nesting near St. Louis. Auk, 26: 434–435.

134. BEYER, L. K. 1938. Nest life of the bank swallow. Wils. Bull., 50: 122–137.

135. BIGGLESTONE, H. C. 1913. A study of the nesting behavior of the yellow warbler (Dendroica aestiva aestiva). Wils. Bull., 25: 49–67.

136. BILDERSEE, I. 1904. Notes on the nesting of the Lawrence's warbler. Bird-Lore, 6: 131–132.

137. BINNEWIES, F. W. 1943. Ferry boat attracts prothonotary warblers. Kentucky Warb., 19: 53–54.

138. BLACK, J. D. 1929. A catbird bush. Ool., 46: 96.

139. BLACKMORE, A. B. 1895. The hooded warbler. Ool., 12: 119–121.

140. BLAIR, C. H. 1943. Bird watching from a blind. Jack-Pine Warb., 21: 74–77.

141. BLAKE, C. H. 1947. Swallow notes. Bull. Mass. Aud. Soc., 31: 239.

142. BLAKE, E. R. 1949. The nest of the Colima warbler in Texas. Wils. Bull., 61: 65–67.

143. BLAKE, F. G. 1907. The nesting of Stelgidopteryx serripennis in Norwich, Vt. Auk, 24: 103–104.

144. BLANCHARD, B. D. 1936. Continuity of behavior in the Nuttall white-crowned sparrow. Condor, 38: 145–150.

145. ———. 1941. The white-crowned sparrows (Zonotrichia leucophrys) of the Pacific seaboard: Environment and annual cycle. Univ. of Calif. Publ. in Zool., 46: 1–178.

146. BLEITZ, D. 1951. Nest of pygmy nuthatch attended by four parents. Condor, 53: 150–151.

147. BLINCOE, B. J. 1921. Two Bachman's sparrow's nests near Bardstown, Kentucky. Wils. Bull., 33: 100–101.

148. BLOCHER, A. 1934. An American tragedy. Ool., 51: 91–92.

149. BODENSTEN, A. J. 1932. A true story of a crippled robin, its mate, young, and a sparrow. Ool., 49: 64–65.

150. BOGGS, M. A. 1926. Marriage relations of a red-eyed towhee. Auk, 43: 242–244.

151. BOLANDER, L. 1907. Birds observed from Marysville to Grass Valley. Condor, 9: 22–27.

152. BOLE, M. 1906. My chickadee family. Bird-Lore, 8: 6–8.

153. BOND, J. 1937. The Cape May warbler in Maine. Auk, 54: 306–308.

154. ———. 1945. The wood warblers. Aud. Mag., 47: 67–73.

155. ———. 1948. Domestic brown creepers. Bull. Maine Aud. Soc., 4: 3–4.

156. BOOK, R. D. 1920. A gnatcatcher's troubles. Bird-Lore, 22: 208–210.

157. BOWDISH, B. S. 1891. Breeding of the mourning warbler in Ontario County, N. Y. Auk, 8: 396.

158. ———. 1894. Grasshopper sparrows in Ontario Co., N. Y. Ool., 11: 336–337.

159. ———. 1907. The rose-breasted grosbeak. Bird-Lore, 9: 110–113.

160. BOWDISH, B. S., AND P. B. PHILIPP. 1916. The Tennessee warbler in New Brunswick. Auk, 33: 1–8.

161. BOWLES, C. W. 1899. Oregon towhee's nest. Osprey, 3: 140.

162. ———. 1902. Notes on the black-throated gray warbler. Condor, 4: 82–85.

163. BOWLES, J. H. 1900. Nesting of the streaked horned lark. Condor, 2: 30–31.

164. ———. 1909. The western winter wren in Washington. Ool., 26: 68–71.

165. BOWMAN, B. L. 1960. Notes on a successful bluebird nest. Oriole, 25: 48.

166. BOYCE, C. 1874. The robin. Am. Nat., 8: 203–208.

167. BOYER, E. 1906. The mocker. Amer. Ornith., 6: 154–157.

168. BRACKBILL, H. 1943. A nesting study of the wood thrush. Wils. Bull., 55: 73–87.

169. ———. 1944a. Juvenile cardinal helping at a nest. Wils. Bull., 56: 50.

170. ———. 1944b. Normal and inverted courtship feeding by the robin. Auk, 61: 138–139.

171. ———. 1947. Period of dependency in the American robin. Wils. Bull., 59: 114–115.
172. ———. 1949. Courtship feeding by the Carolina chickadee and tufted titmouse. Auk, 66: 290–292.
173. ———. 1950. Successive nest sites of individual birds of eight species. Bird-Banding, 21: 6–8.
174. ———. 1952. A joint nesting of cardinals and song sparrows. Auk, 69: 302–307.
175. ———. 1958. Nesting behavior of the wood thrush. Wils. Bull., 70: 70–89.
176. BRADBURY, W. C. 1917. Notes on the nesting habits of the Clarke nutcracker in Colorado. Condor, 19: 149–155.
177. BRADLEY, H. L. 1940. A few observations on the nesting of the eastern chipping sparrow. Jack-Pine Warb., 18: 35–46.
178. ———. 1948. A life history study of the indigo bunting. Jack-Pine Warb., 26: 103–113.
179. BRANDT, A. E. 1947. The rearing of a cowbird by Acadian flycatchers. Wils. Bull., 59: 79–82.
180. BRANDT, H. 1940. Texas bird adventures. Bird Research Foundation, Cleveland, Ohio. 192 pp.
181. ———. 1951. Arizona and its bird life. Bird Research Foundation, Cleveland, Ohio. 723 pp.
182. BRECHER, L. C. 1940. Late record of the red-breasted nuthatch. Kentucky Warb., 16: 31.
183. ———. 1946. Notes on the nesting of the scarlet tanager. Kentucky Warb., 22: 46–50.
184. BRENINGER, G. F. 1894. American and Mexican crossbills. Nidol., 1: 99–101.
185. BREWER, R. 1961. Comparative notes on the life history of the Carolina chickadee. Wils. Bull., 73: 348–373.
186. ———. 1963. Ecological and reproductive relationships of black-capped and Carolina chickadees. Auk, 80: 9–47.
187. BREWER, R., AND A. RAIM. 1965. Summer observations of Nashville and black-throated green warblers in Kalamazoo County, Mich. Jack-Pine Warb., 43: 169.
188. BREWER, T. M. 1880. The nesting of the common crossbill. Bull. Nutt. Orn. Club, 5: 50–51.
189. BREWSTER, W. 1878. The prothonotary warbler (Protonotaria citrea). Bull. Nutt. Orn. Club, 3: 153–162.
190. ———. 1879a. Notes upon the distribution, habits, and nesting of the black-capped vireo (Vireo atricapillus). Bull. Nutt. Orn. Club, 4: 99–103.
191. ———. 1879b. Breeding habits of the American brown creeper (Certhia familiaris americana). Bull. Nutt. Orn. Club, 4: 199–209.
192. ———. 1886. An ornithological reconnaissance in western North Carolina. Auk, 3: 173–179.
193. ———. 1888. Breeding of the golden-crested kinglet (Regulus satrapa) in Worcester County, Massachusetts, with a description of its nest and eggs. Auk, 5: 337–344.
194. ———. 1903. Further notes on the Philadelphia vireo, with description of the nest and eggs. Auk, 20: 369–376.
195. ———. 1905. Notes on the breeding of Bachman's warbler, Helminthophila bachmanii (Aud.), near Charleston, South Carolina, with a description of the first plumage of the species. Auk, 22: 392–394.
196. ———. 1907. Breeding of the rough-winged swallow in Berkshire County, Massachusetts. Auk, 24: 221–222.
197. ———. 1937. The birds of the Lake Umbagog Region of Maine. Bull. Mus. Comp. Zool., Harvard, 66: 403–521.
198. BRIGHAM, E. M., JR. 1942. The blue-headed vireo nests in Michigan. Jack-Pine Warb., 20: 67–72.
199. ———. 1943. Bird watching from a blind. I. The prairie marsh wren. Jack-Pine Warb., 21: 7–11.
200. ———. 1954. Photograph of male Kirtland's warbler. Bull. Mass. Aud. Soc., 38: 3.
201. BRIMLEY, C. S. 1889. Nesting of the blue-gray gnat-catcher at Raleigh, N. C. Ornith. and Ool., 14: 181–182.
202. ———. 1890. The nesting of the yellow-throated warbler at Raleigh, N. C. Auk, 7: 323–326.

203. ———. 1891. On the breeding habits of *Dendroica vigorsii* at Raleigh, North Carolina. Auk, 8: 199–200.

204. BRODRICK, H. J. 1938. Nesting and re-mating of a pair of bluebirds. Auk, 55: 538–539.

205. BROOKS, M. 1933. Taming the blue-gray gnatcatchers. Bird-Lore, 35: 90–93.

206. ———. 1938. Bachman's sparrow in the north-central portion of its range. Wils. Bull., 50: 86–109.

207. BROOKS, W. S. 1915. Notes on birds from east Siberia and Arctic Alaska. Bull. Mus. Comp. Zool., Harvard, 59: 361–413.

208. BROWN, B. L. 1931. Mockingbirds nesting in Bangor, Maine. Bird-Lore, 33: 241–245.

209. BROWN, D. E. 1931. Additional notes on the nesting habits of the Steller jay (*Cyanocitta stelleri stelleri*). Murrelet, 12: 57.

210. BROWN, J. L. 1963a. Social organization and behavior of the Mexican jay. Condor, 65: 126–153.

211. ———. 1963b. Aggressiveness, dominance and social organization in the Steller jay. Condor, 65: 460–484.

212. BROWNELL, C. L. 1904. The warblers of the Lower Hudson Valley. Warbler, 2 (old series): 26–27.

213. BROWNELL, L. W. 1904. The architecture of birds. Warbler, 2 (old series): 8–13.

214. ———. 1919. The wood thrush. Blue Bird, 11: 122–123.

215. BROWNELL, S. P. 1910. My summer tenants. Bird-Lore, 12: 95–100.

216. BRUCE, M. E. 1898. A month with the goldfinches. Auk, 15: 239–243.

217. BRYANT, L., JR. 1931. Some notes on the breeding of the vesper sparrow. Bird-Banding, 2: 178–184.

218. BRYENS, O. M. 1925. Statistics on the house wren. Wils. Bull., 37: 157–159.

219. BUCHWALD, MRS. C. A. 1957. Rough-winged swallows nesting in Newry, Maine. Maine Field Nat., 13: 89.

220. BUCK, H. R. 1896. The breeding of warbling and yellow-throated vireos. Wils. Bull., 8(11): 4–5.

221. BUELL, B. G. 1939. Ornithology through a window. Jack-Pine Warb., 17: 27–33.

222. BUMANN, C. S. 1931. Habits of the kingbird. Ool., 48: 30.

223. BUNKER, C. D. 1910. Habits of the black-capt vireo (*Vireo atricapillus*). Condor, 12: 70–73.

224. BURGESS, T. W. 1958. Attracting birds with doughnuts. Bull. Mass. Aud. Soc., 43: 36.

225. BURNS, F. L. 1905. The worm-eating warbler. Bird-Lore, 7: 137–139.

226. ———. 1915. Comparative periods of deposition and incubation of some North American birds. Wils. Bull., 27: 275–286.

227. ———. 1937. The song periods of some common southeastern Pennsylvania birds in comparison with their seasonal reproductive cycles. Ool., 54: 114–130.

228. BURNS, R. D. 1963. Michigan cooperative cardinal study nesting data. Jack-Pine Warb., 41: 56–61.

229. BURROUGHS, J. 1901. A bewildered phoebe. Bird-Lore, 3: 85–87.

230. BURTCH, V. 1900. Louisiana water-thrush. Ool., 17: 7–8.

231. ———. 1910. Nesting of the black-throated green warbler. Ool., 27: 58–61.

232. ———. 1918. Notes on the tree swallow. Bird-Lore, 20: 133–135.

233. BUTTRICK, P. L. 1909. Observations on the life history of the bobolink. Bird-Lore, 11: 125–126.

234. BUTTS, W. K. 1931a. A study of the chickadee and white-breasted nuthatch by means of marked individuals. Part II. The chickadee (*Penthestes atricapillus atricapillus*). Bird-Banding, 2: 1–26.

235. ———. 1931b. A study of the chickadee and white-breasted nuthatch by means of marked individuals. Part III. The white-breasted nuthatch (*Sitta carolinensis cookei*). Bird-Banding, 2: 59–76.

236. CADE, T. J. 1962. Wing movements, hunting, and displays of the northern shrike. Wils. Bull., 74: 386–408.

237. CAHN, A. R. 1913. The birds of Waukesha County, Wisconsin. Bull. Wis. Nat. Hist. Society, 11: 113–149.

238. CAIRNS, J. S. 1889. The summer birds of Buncombe County, North Carolina. Ornith. and Ool., 14: 17–23.

239. ———. 1896. The summer home of *Dendroica caerulescens*. Papers presented to the World's Congress on Ornithology, Chicago. *In*: Chapman, 1907.

240. CAMERON, E. S. 1907. The birds of Custer and Dawson Counties, Montana. Auk, 24: 241–270, 389–406.

241. ———. 1908. The birds of Custer and Dawson Counties, Montana. Auk, 25: 39–56.

242. CAMPBELL, L. W. 1928. The chestnut-sided warbler nesting near Toledo, Ohio. Wils. Bull., 40: 253.

243. ———. 1933. Nesting of the mourning warbler near Toledo, Ohio. Auk, 50: 117–118.

244. ———. 1938. The Canada warbler breeding near Toledo, Ohio. Wils. Bull., 50: 61.

245. CANFIELD, J. B. 1902. Louisiana water thrush. Amer. Ornith., 2: 225–227.

246. CANNON, A. I. 1923. A wood thrush story. Bird-Lore, 25: 320–321.

247. CAREY, H. R. 1925. How a family of hermit thrushes came to camp. Bird-Lore, 27: 225–228.

248. CARRIKER, M. A., JR. 1901. Notes on the breeding of the prothonotary warbler. Proc. Nebraska Ornith. Union, 2: 42–44.

249. CARTER, T. D. 1928. History of a female hooded warbler. Bull. N.E. Bird-Banding Assoc., 4: 95–97.

250. ———. 1944. Six years with a Brewster's warbler. Auk, 61: 48–61.

251. CARTER, T. D., AND R. H. HOWLAND. 1923. A Brewster's warbler and his brood. Auk, 40: 423–430.

252. CARTWRIGHT, B. W., T. M. SHORTT, AND R. D. HARRIS. 1937. Baird's sparrow. Trans. Roy. Can. Inst., 21: 153–197.

253. CASE, N. A. 1962. Nesting and flocking of the redwinged blackbird. Ph.D. dissertation, Cornell Univ. Library, Ithaca, New York.

254. CASE, N. A., AND O. H. HEWITT. 1963. Nesting and productivity of the red-winged blackbird in relation to habitat. Living Bird, 2: 7–20.

255. CASH, J. A. 1933. Tree swallows: some observations made at close quarters. Bird-Lore, 35: 201–205.

256. CASWELL, A. 1889. The rose-breasted grosbeak, *Habia ludoviciana*. Ornith. and Ool. Semi-annual (Wils. Bull.), 1 (2): 23–24.

257. CHACE, L. W. 1928. Another martin story. Ool., 45: 154–156.

258. CHADBOURNE, A. P. 1905. Nesting habits of the brown creeper as observed in Plymouth County, Massachusetts, with description of a nest from North Scituate. Auk, 22: 179–183.

259. CHAMBERLAIN, B. R. 1954. Goldfinches nesting at Rocky Mount, N. C. Chat, 18: 54–55.

260. ———. 1960. Brown creeper nest at High Hampton. Chat, 24: 102.

261. CHAMBERLAIN, N. M. 1946. A cardinal family. Flicker, 18: 12–13.

262. CHAMBERLIN, C. 1901. Some architectural traits of the western gnatcatcher (*Polioptila caerulea obscura*). Condor, 3: 33–36.

263. CHAPMAN, F. M. 1894. On the birds of the island of Trinidad. Bull. Am. Mus. Nat. Hist., 6: 1–86.

264. ———. 1897. Preliminary descriptions of new birds from Mexico and Arizona. Auk, 14: 310–311.

265. ———. 1901. Bird nesting with Burroughs. Bird-Lore, 3: 88–93.

266. ———. 1907. The warblers of North America. D. Appleton and Co., New York. 306 pp.

267. CHAPMAN, L. B. 1935. Studies of a tree swallow colony. Bird-Banding, 6: 45–57.

268. ———. 1939. Studies of a tree swallow colony (second paper). Bird-Banding, 10: 61–72.

269. ———. 1955. Studies of a tree swallow colony (third paper). Bird-Banding, 26: 45–70.

270. CHASE, V. H. 1899. Rose-breasted grosbeak. Wils. Bull., 11: 54–55.

271. CHAPIN, M. L. 1955. Robins at Crane Cottage. Bull. Mass. Aud. Soc., 39: 281–284.

272. CHRIST, J. C. 1958. Some observations of the nesting habits of the eastern phoebe. Nebraska Bird Review, 26: 34–38.

273. ———. 1962. Activity at a phoebe nest. Flicker, 34: 102.

274. CHRISTY, B. H. 1926. Notes. Cardinal, 1 (8): 18–21.

275. ———. 1930. An English sparrow foster parent. Cardinal, 2: 191–192.

276. CLARK, J. H. 1898. Notes on the nesting of Palmer's thrasher at El Plomo, Sonora, Mexico. Auk, 15: 272–274.
277. ———. 1899. Nesting of the white-necked raven in giant cactus. Osprey, 3: 78.
278. ———. 1904. Curve-billed and Palmer's thrashers. Auk, 21: 214–217.
279. CLARK, J. N. 1882. Hooded warbler. Nesting in southern Conn. Ornith. and Ool., 7: 102.
280. ———. 1887. Nesting of the black-throated green warbler. Ornith. and Ool., 12: 22–23.
281. ———. 1890. Nesting of the yellow-throated vireo. Ornith. and Ool., 15: 69–70.
282. ———. 1895. Chickadee. Nidol., 2: 88–90.
283. CLAY, F. W. 1888. Nesting of the cardinal grosbeak. Ool., 5: 39–40.
284. CLAY, M. B. 1925. The prothonotary warbler at North Bristol, Trumbull County, Ohio. Wils. Bull., 37: 225.
285. CLAYTON, J. W. 1907. Field notes from Upper Penobscot, Maine. Warbler, 3 (series 2): 15–18.
286. CLEVELAND, L. 1903. Nesting of the indigo bunting. Bird-Lore, 5: 87–88.
287. CLOTFELTER, J. W. 1946. Some episodes in the lives of robins. Kentucky Warb., 22: 20–22.
288. COBB, S. 1904. Nesting of a golden-crowned kinglet in Massachusetts. Amer. Ornith., 4: 138–140.
289. COFFEY, J. W. 1964. Breeding of the Traill's flycatcher in Virginia. Raven, 35: 60–61.
290. COFFIN, L. V. B. 1915. Nesting habits of Kentucky warbler. Wils. Bull., 27: 348.
291. COMBELLACK, C. R. B. 1954. A nesting of violet-green swallows. Auk, 71: 435–442.
292. COMEAU, C. M. 1954. Black-throated green warbler nesting. Chat, 18: 81–82.
293. COMFORT, J. E. 1944. The parula warbler. Blue Bird, 11: 54–55.
294. COMFORT, H. B. 1947. Bachman's sparrow. Blue Bird, 14: 3.
295. COMMON, M. A. 1934. Notes on a red-eyed vireo's nest. Auk, 51: 241–242.
296. ———. 1947. The robin nests. Auk, 64: 238–245.
297. CONNETT, J. A. 1937. Region No. 1. Blue Bird, 4: 88–89.
298. COOK, MRS. H. P. 1932. The blue-gray gnatcatcher in Indiana. Wils. Bull., 44: 45.
299. ———. 1934. A close up of the cardinal. Wils. Bull., 46: 260–261.
300. ———. 1937. Experiences with cardinals. 1937 Indiana Aud. Soc. Yearbook: 42–45.
301. COOKMAN, A. 1911. The willow goldfinch (Astragalina tristis salicamans). Ool., 28: 117–118.
302. COOLEY, E. 1909. Yellow-breasted chat. Wils. Bull., 21: 41–42.
303. COOPER, J. G. 1876a. Californian garden birds. Am. Nat., 10: 90–96.
304. ———. 1876b. Nesting habits of the California house wren (Troglodytes aedon var. parkmanni). Bull. Nuttall Orn. Club, 1: 79–81.
305. COOPER, M. D. 1893. Oven birds nest building. Ool., 10: 307.
306. COPELAND, W. F. 1909. An exercise in bird study. Wils. Bull., 21: 40–45.
307. CORDIER, A. H. 1923. Birds. Their photographs and home life. Dorrance, Phila-delphia. 247 pp.
308. ———. 1927. Some observations on the water ouzel. Auk, 44: 169–178.
309. COTRILLE, B. D. 1962. A search for nesting Cape May warblers. Flicker, 34: 38–40.
310. COTTINGHAM, A. 1925. The robin's nest. Bird-Lore, 27: 182–183.
311. COUES, E. 1878a. The eave, cliff or crescent swallow (Petrochelidon lunifrons). Bull. Nutt. Orn. Club, 3: 105–112.
312. ———. 1878b. Birds of the Colorado Valley, first part. U. S. Geol. Survey of the Territories, Misc. Pub., 11: 1–807.
313. ———. 1878c. Nest and eggs of Helminthophaga pinus. Bull. Nutt. Orn. Club, 3: 194.
314. COUTLEE, E. L. 1967. Agonistic behavior in the American goldfinch. Wils. Bull., 79: 89–109.
315. COVELL, H. H. 1922. Home life of the purple finch. Bird-Lore, 24: 212–213.
316. COWAN, I. McT. 1939. The vertebrate fauna of the Peace River District of British Columbia. Occas. Papers Brit. Col. Prov. Mus., 1: 1–102.
317. COX, G. W. 1960. A life history of the mourning warbler. Wils. Bull., 72: 5–28.
318. CRABB, E. D. 1923. Notes on the nesting of a pair of dickcissels (Spiza americana). Auk, 40: 606–609.
319. CRAIGMILE, E. A. 1939. Prairie warblers nesting. Bull. Illinois Aud. Soc., 31: 9.

320. CRIDDLE, N. 1920. Notes on the nesting habits and food of prairie horned larks in Manitoba. Can. Field Nat., 34: 14–16.
321. ———. 1927. Habits of the mountain bluebird in Manitoba. Can. Field Nat., 41: 40–44.
322. CRIDDLE, N., AND S. CRIDDLE. 1917. Horned larks at Aweme, Manitoba. Ottawa Nat., 30: 144–148.
323. CROOKS, M. P., AND G. O. HENDRICKSON. 1953. Field sparrow life history in central Iowa. Iowa Bird Life, 23: 10–13.
324. CROSS, F. C. 1951. Courtship feeding of Rocky Mountain pine grosbeak, *Pinicola enucleator*. Auk, 68: 110–111.
325. CROUCH, J. E. 1936. Nesting habits of the cedar waxwing. Auk, 53: 1–8.
326. CRUICKSHANK, A. D. 1937. A few warbler observations. Proc. Linn. Soc. N. Y., 49: 70–71.
327. ———. 1950. Crossbills—unpredictable birds of the North. Aud. Mag., 52: 9–13.
328. CRUICKSHANK, H. G. 1951. New bird discoveries at the Audubon Camp of Maine. Aud. Mag., 53: 188–193.
329. CUTHBERT, N. L. 1962. The Michigan Audubon Society phoebe study (Part II). Jack-Pine Warb., 40: 68–83.
330. DALES, M. 1926. A house wren study. Wils. Bull., 38: 14–16.
331. DALES, M., AND W. W. BENNETT. 1929. Nesting of the pine siskin in Iowa with remarks on regurgitative feeding. Wils. Bull., 41: 74–77.
332. DANIEL, J. W., JR. 1901. Life history of the prairie warbler (*Dendroica discolor*). Osprey, 5: 118–119.
333. DAUBENDIEK, R. W. 1965. Baltimore orioles nesting near the Sherman Swift Tower, Harpers Ferry, Iowa. Iowa Bird Life, 35: 53–54.
334. DAVISON, S. L. 1889. Breeding of *Habia ludoviciana* in Niagara County, New York. Auk, 6: 191–192.
335. DAVIDSON, W. A. 1897. Vireonidae of Wayne County, Mich. Bull. Mich. Ornith. Club, 1: 6.
336. DAVIE, O. 1904. The purple martin. Amer. Ornith., 4: 260–263.
337. DAVIS, D. E. 1941. The belligerency of the kingbird. Wils. Bull., 53: 157–168.
338. ———. 1942. Descriptive notes on a catbird nest. Bird-Banding, 13: 38–39.
339. ———. 1954. The breeding biology of Hammond's flycatcher. Auk, 71: 164–171.
340. ———. 1959. Observations on territorial behavior of least flycatchers. Wils. Bull., 71: 73–85.
341. DAVIS, E. M. 1937. Observations on nesting barn swallows. Bird-Banding, 8: 66–72.
342. DAVIS, J. 1960. Nesting behavior of the rufous-sided towhee in coastal California. Condor, 62: 434–456.
343. DAVIS, J., G. F. FISLER, AND B. S. DAVIS. 1963. The breeding biology of the western flycatcher. Condor, 65: 337–382.
344. DAVIS, L. I. 1945. Rose-throated becard nesting in Cameron County, Texas. Auk, 62: 316–317.
345. ———. 1957. Observations on Mexican birds. Wils. Bull., 69: 364–367.
346. DAVIS, M. 1931. Magpie breeding in captivity. Auk, 48: 604.
347. ———. 1939. General and mother martin. Chat, 3: 22–24.
348. DAVIS, W. H. 1941. Chickadees nesting in vacant hornets' nest. Ool., 58: 145–146.
349. DAWSON, W. L. 1903. The birds of Ohio. Wheaton Publ. Co., Columbus. 671 pp.
350. ———. 1919. The solitaires of Shasta. Condor, 21: 12–21.
351. DAY, K. C. 1953. Home life of the veery. Bird-Banding, 24: 100–106.
352. DECK, R. S. 1928. A catbird family. Bird-Lore, 30: 101–105.
353. ———. 1934. Feathered philosophers. Bird-Lore, 36: 226–231.
354. DE GARIS, C. F. 1936. Notes on six nests of the Kentucky warbler (*Oporornis formosus*). Auk, 53: 418–428.
355. DE GROOT, D. S. 1935. Nesting of the Pacific evening grosbeak in the vicinity of Echo Lake, Eldorado County, California. Condor, 37: 40–42.
356. DE LONG, MRS. W. C. 1943. Nesting of the blue-gray gnatcatcher. Iowa Bird Life, 13: 51.
357. DENNIS, J. V. 1954. The parula warbler near Leesburg, Virginia. Raven, 25: 102.
358. DENSMORE, M. 1925. A day with a wren family. Bird-Lore, 27: 101–102.
359. DENTON, J. F. 1953. The summer birds of Lookout Mountain, Georgia–Alabama. Oriole, 18: 25–31.
360. ———. 1961. Baltimore oriole breeding in Aiken County, S. C. Chat, 25: 92.

361. DENTON, J. F., AND D. NEAL. 1951. The abundance and distribution of some summer birds of Tray Mountain, Georgia. Oriole, 16: 25–30.

362. DES BRISAY, MRS. M. B. 1918. Our summer visitors—a true story of some Nova Scotian birds. Bird-Lore, 20: 301–302.

363. DEUSING, M. 1942. A range and population study of the purple martin in Wisconsin. Pass. Pigeon, 4: 17–21.

364. DEVINEY, E. 1957. Towhee helps cardinals raise young. Florida Nat., 30: 125.

365. DE WINDT, C. 1956. Newburyport—host to nesting shrikes. Bull. Mass. Aud. Soc., 40: 437–438.

366. DICE, L. R. 1918a. Notes on the nesting of the redpoll. Condor, 20: 129–131.

367. ———. 1918b. The birds of Walla Walla and Columbia Counties, southeastern Washington. Auk, 35: 148–161.

368. DICKERSON, M. C. 1908. Chestnut-sided warbler—a study. Bird-Lore, 10: 207–209.

369. DICKEY, S. S. 1912. The Bewick's wren. Ool., 29: 299–301.

370. ———. 1914. Nesting of the white-breasted nuthatch in central Pennsylvania. Ool., 31: 66–67.

371. ———. 1915. The blue-gray gnatcatcher. Ool., 32: 67–71.

372. ———. 1938. The white-eyed vireo in Greene County, Pennsylvania. Cardinal, 4: 158–163.

373. DICKINSON, F. R. 1933. A pair of waxwings. Aud. Ann. Bull., 23: 25–26.

374. DIETRICH, E. J. 1914. Some notes on Macgillivray's warbler. Ool., 31: 105–111.

375. DIKE, A. C. 1903. A phoebe with three nests. Bird-Lore, 5: 198.

376. DILL, H. R. 1902. One yellow warbler family. Jour. Maine Ornith. Soc., 4: 14–16.

377. DIXON, J. B. 1934. Nesting of the Clark nutcracker in California. Condor, 36: 229–234.

378. ———. 1936. Nesting of the Sierra Nevada rosy finch. Condor, 38: 3–8.

379. DIXON, J. S. 1938. Birds and mammals of Mount McKinley National Park, Alaska. Parks Fauna Series, 3: 1–236.

380. ———. 1943. Birds observed between Point Barrow and Herschel Island on the Arctic coast of Alaska. Condor, 45: 49–57.

381. DIXON, K. L. 1949. Behavior of the plain titmouse. Condor, 51: 110–136.

382. ———. 1955. An ecological analysis of the interbreeding of crested titmice in Texas. Univ. Calif. Publ. Zool., 54: 125–205.

383. DOAN, W. D. 1889. The blue jay, Cyanocitta cristata. Ornith. and Ool. Semiannual (Wils. Bull.), 1: 10–12.

384. DODGE, M. L. 1897. A peculiar site for an oriole's nest. Ool., 14: 17–18.

385. DOLLAR, S. 1928. History of a cardinal family. Bird-Lore, 30: 118.

386. DONAHUE, R. J. 1933. Trail of the seasons. Ool., 50: 112.

387. DOWNS, E. H. 1954. Nesting evening grosbeaks in Vermont. Bull. Mass. Aud. Soc., 38: 11–15.

388. DRAPER, S. L. 1904. Bluebirds. Warbler, 2 (first series): 92.

389. DREW, F. M. 1881. Field notes on the birds of San Juan County, Colorado. Bull. Nuttall Orn. Club, 6: 85–91.

390. DRUM, M. 1939. Territorial studies on the eastern goldfinch. Wils. Bull., 51: 69–77.

391. DRURY, W. H., JR. 1961. Studies of the breeding biology of horned lark, water pipit, Lapland longspur, and snow bunting on Bylot Island, Northwest Territories, Canada. Bird-Banding, 32: 1–46.

392. DU BOIS, A. D. 1923. Two nest-studies of McCown's longspur. Bird-Lore, 25: 95–105.

393. ———. 1936. Habits and nest life of the desert horned lark. Condor, 38: 49–56.

394. ———. 1937. The McCown longspurs of a Montana prairie. Condor, 39: 233–238.

395. ———. 1940. Nesting habits and behavior of Bell's vireo. Aud. Bull., 35: 1–8.

396. DUNHAM, E. M. 1926. Experiences in banding rose-breasted grosbeaks. Bull. N. E. Bird-Banding Assoc., 2: 88.

397. DUNN, H. H. 1906. Western lark sparrow. Ool., 23: 169–170.

398. ———. 1907. Brewer's blackbird. Ool., 24: 55–57.

399. DUNN, N. 1957. Lazuli bunting nesting at Moose Jaw. Blue Jay, 15: 147.

400. DURAND, F. V. 1939. Observations on the nesting habits of the loggerhead shrike. Migrant, 10: 35.

401. DURY, C. 1877. Fecundity of the Carolina wren (Thryothorus ludovicianus). Bull. Nuttall Orn. Club, 2: 50.

402. DUTCHER, W. 1905. The American goldfinch. Bird-Lore, 7: 290–293.
403. E., W. T. 1884. The American redstart. Young Ool., 1: 119.
404. EARLY, R. N. 1952. The Florida jay. Florida Nat., 25: 57–58.
405. EATON, S. W. 1957. A life history study of *Seiurus noveboracensis*. Sci. Studies of St. Bonaventure Univ., 19: 7–36.
406. ———. 1958. A life history study of the Louisiana waterthrush. Wils. Bull., 70: 211–236.
407. EDGAR, M. 1943. Tufted titmouse nesting in Minnesota. Flicker, 15: 35.
408. EDSON, J. M. 1930. Recession in weight of nestling birds. Condor, 32: 137–141.
409. EGAN, T. J. 1889. Nesting of the American crossbill. Ornith. and Ool., 14: 89–90.
410. EKBLAW, W. E. 1919. The snow bunting, an Arctic study in black and white. Wils. Bull., 31: 41–45.
411. ELLIOTT, H. H. 1933. The intelligence of a robin. Cardinal, 3: 130–131.
412. ELLIOTT, H. W. 1881. The seal-islands of Alaska. U. S. Gov't Printing Office, Washington, D. C. 176 pp.
413. ELLIOTT, J. J. 1950. Additional notes on the parula warbler (*Compsothlypis americana*) on Long Island. Birds of Long Island, 6: 164–166.
414. ELLIOTT, M. D. 1941. Some observations on nesting water ouzels. Jack-Pine Warb., 19: 64.
415. ELLIS, J. V., JR. 1923. Some Yakima County, Washington, notes. Murrelet, 4(2): 17–18.
416. EMERSON, G. 1954. The barn swallow in the Midwest. Aud. Mag., 56: 164–167.
417. EMLEN, J. T., JR. 1952. Social behavior in nesting cliff swallows. Condor, 54: 177–199.
418. ———. 1954. Territory, nest building, and pair formation in the cliff swallow. Auk, 71: 16–35.
419. ERICKSON, M. M. 1938. Territory, annual cycle, and numbers in a population of wren-tits (*Chamaea fasciata*). Univ. Calif. Publ. Zool., 42: 247–333.
420. ERWIN, W. G. 1935. Some nesting habits of the brown thrasher. Jour. Tenn. Acad. Sci., 10: 179–204.
421. ESTEN, S. R. 1925. A comparative study of the nest life of the towhee, meadowlark, and rose-breasted grosbeak. Proc. Indiana Acad. Sci., 34: 397–401.
422. EVENDEN, F. G., JR. 1947. Nesting studies of the black-billed magpie in southern Idaho. Auk, 64: 260–266.
423. EVENDEN, F. G. 1957. Observations on nesting behavior of the house finch. Condor, 59: 112–117.
424. EVERMAN, B. W. 1882. Black-crested flycatcher. Ornith. and Ool., 7: 169–170, 177–179.
425. EYER, L. E. 1954. A life history study of the bronzed grackle, *Quiscalus quiscula versicolor* Vieillot. Dissert. Abstr., 19(2): 3057–3058.
426. ———. 1963. Observations on golden-winged warblers at Itasca State Park, Minnesota. Jack-Pine Warb., 41: 96–109.
427. FABENS, M. E. 1919. Interlopers. Bird-Lore, 21: 304–305.
428. FALLS, J. B. 1959. Report to National Research Council Grant Committee of Canada.
429. FARNER, D. S. 1952. The birds of Crater Lake National Park. Univ. of Kansas Press, Lawrence. 187 pp.
430. FAUTIN, R. W. 1940. The establishment and maintenance of territories by the yellow-headed blackbird in Utah. Great Basin Nat., 1: 75–91.
431. ———. 1941a. Incubation studies of the yellow-headed blackbird. Wils. Bull., 53: 107–122.
432. ———. 1941b. Development of nestling yellow-headed blackbirds. Auk, 58: 215–232.
433. FAXON, W. 1911. Brewster's warbler. Mem. Mus. Comp. Zool., Harvard, 40: 57–78.
434. ———. 1915. Junco breeding in Concord and Lexington, Mass. Auk, 32: 497.
435. FERNALD, R. H. 1890. Nesting of the red-breasted nuthatch in Orono, Maine. Ornith. and Ool., 15: 40–41.
436. FESER, MRS. A. L. 1928. Bird notes from the northwood. Aud. Ann. Bull., 19: 22–24.
437. FICKEN, M. S. 1964. Nest-site selection in the American redstart. Wils. Bull., 76: 189–190.

438. FICKEN, R. W. 1963. Courtship and agonistic behavior of the common grackle, *Quiscalus quiscula*. Auk, 80: 52–72.
439. FINKLEA, I., AND A. L. MORRIS. 1913. A study of mockingbirds. Bird-Lore, 15: 307–308.
440. FINLEY, W. L. 1903. Two vireos caught with a camera. Condor, 5: 61–64.
441. ———. 1904a. Two Oregon warblers. Condor, 6: 31–35.
442. ———. 1904b. The black-headed grosbeak. Condor, 6: 145–148.
443. ———. 1905. A study in bird confidence. Condor, 7: 91–94.
444. ———. 1906. The chickadee at home. Condor, 8: 63–67.
445. ———. 1907a. American birds studied and photographed from life. Chas. Scribner's Sons, New York. 256 pp.
446. ———. 1907b. Do birds desert young? Condor, 9: 59–60.
447. ———. 1907c. Two studies in blue. Condor, 9: 121–127.
448. ———. 1909. The bush-tit. Bird-Lore, 11: 225–228.
449. FISHER, A. K. 1883. Nesting of *Chrysomitris pinus* at Sing Sing, N. Y. Bull. Nuttall Orn. Club, 8: 180–181.
450. FISKE, G. W., JR. 1905. The olive-sided flycatcher. Bird-Lore, 7: 195–196.
451. FITCH, F. W., JR. 1950. Life history and ecology of the scissor-tailed flycatcher, *Muscivora forficata*. Auk, 67: 145–168.
452. FITCH, H. S. 1958. Home ranges, territories, and seasonal movements of vertebrates of the Natural History Reservation. Univ. of Kansas Publ. Mus. Nat. Hist., 11: 63–326.
453. FITCH, H. S., AND V. R. FITCH. 1955. Observations on the summer tanager in northeastern Kansas. Wils. Bull., 67: 45–54.
454. FLEMING, J. H. 1919. Birds of northern Saskatchewan and northern Manitoba collected in 1914 by Capt. Angus Buchanan. Can. Field Nat., 33: 109–113.
455. FLETCHER, L. B. 1944. Unusual nesting of house wrens. Bird-Banding, 15: 160–161.
456. FOOT, N. C. 1916. Junco breeding at West Quincy, Mass. Auk, 33: 436.
457. FORBUSH, E. H. 1907. Useful birds and their protection. Wright and Potter Printing Co., Boston. 437 pp.
458. ———. 1911. The cedar waxwing. Bird-Lore, 13: 55–58.
459. ———. 1912. The chickadee. Bird-Lore, 14: 372–375.
460. ———. 1927. Birds of Massachusetts and other New England states, Vol. 2. Norwood Press, Norwood, Mass. 461 pp.
461. ———. 1929. Birds of Massachusetts and other New England states, Vol. 3. Norwood Press, Norwood, Mass. 466 pp.
462. FOWLER, A. 1868. The chickadee. Am. Nat., 1: 584–587.
463. FOX, G. A. 1961. A contribution to the life history of the clay-colored sparrow. Auk, 78: 220–224.
464. FREELAND, D. B. 1960. Central New York "Big Run." Bull. Mass. Aud. Soc., 44: 255–256.
465. FREI, M. L. 1940. Peeps into the private life of a pair of pewees. Kentucky Warb., 16: 33–34.
466. FRENCH, N. R. 1959. Life history of the black rosy finch. Auk, 76: 159–180.
467. FUCHS, E. A. 1948. Yellow warbler feeds young catbirds. Bull. Mass. Aud. Soc., 32: 278.
468. GABRIELSON, I. N. 1912. A study of the home life of the brown thrasher, *Toxostoma rufum* (Linn.). Wils. Bull., 24: 65–94.
469. ———. 1913. Nest life of the catbird. Wils. Bull., 25: 166–187.
470. ———. 1914. Ten days' bird study in a Nebraska swamp. Wils. Bull., 26: 51–68.
471. ———. 1915a. Field observations on the rose-breasted grosbeak. Wils. Bull., 27: 357–368.
472. ———. 1915b. The home of the great crest. Wils. Bull., 27: 421–434.
473. ———. 1922. Short notes on the life histories of various species of birds. Wils. Bull., 34: 193–210.
474. GABRIELSON, I. N., AND F. C. LINCOLN. 1959. The birds of Alaska. Stackpole Co., Harrisburg, Pa., and Wildlife Management Inst., Washington, D. C. 922 pp.
475. GAGE, G. 1961. A pair of mockingbirds at Clemson. Chat, 25: 47–50.
476. GALLUP, F. 1917. A substitute for a hollow limb. Bird-Lore, 19: 139–141.
477. GANDER, F. F. 1922. The brown-headed nuthatch. Bird-Lore, 24: 328–330.
478. ———. 1927. Phainopepla notes. Bird-Lore, 29: 420–421.
479. ———. 1957. The brown towhee. Aud. Mag., 59: 124–127.

480. ———. 1958. The house finch. Aud. Mag., 60: 172–173.
481. ———. 1959. The mockingbirds of Kissing Rocks Garden. Aud. Mag., 61: 168–169, 182–184.
482. ———. 1960. Western bluebirds in my garden. Aud. Mag., 62: 70–71, 83.
483. Ganier, A. F. 1933. A ten-year-old cardinal. Wils. Bull., 45: 152–154.
484. ———. 1934. Further notes on a very old cardinal. Wils. Bull., 46: 236–237.
485. ———. 1935. The cardinal now twelve years old. Wils. Bull., 47: 285–286.
486. ———. 1937. Further notes on a very old cardinal. Wils. Bull., 49: 15–16.
487. ———. 1941. Through the seasons with the cardinal. Migrant, 12: 1–4.
488. Gardner, Mrs. A. F. 1920. A confusion of instincts. Bird-Lore, 22: 164.
489. Gardner, B. V. 1933. The persistence of a house wren. Bird-Lore, 35: 151–152.
490. Gaulding, W., Jr. 1944. Crested flycatchers nesting in gourds. Oriole, 9: 13.
491. Gentry, T. G. 1876. Life-histories of the birds of eastern Pennsylvania, Vol. 1. Published by the author, Philadelphia. 399 pp.
492. ———. 1877. Life-histories of the birds of eastern Pennsylvania, Vol. 2. Naturalists' Agency, Salem, Mass. 336 pp.
493. Getty, B. M. 1924. A robin story. Ool., 41: 102–103.
494. Gianini, C. A. 1917. Some Alaska Peninsula bird notes. Auk, 34: 394–402.
495. Gibbs, M. 1894. Nesting habits of the chestnut-sided warbler. Ool., 11: 331–333.
496. ———. 1896. The bronzed grackle. Ool., 13: 32–34.
497. ———. 1899. Real estate owners. Ool., 16: 182–183.
498. ———. 1902. The nesting of birds. Ool., 19: 103–104, 150–152.
499. Gignoux, C. 1924. Nesting of pigmy nuthatches at Lake Tahoe. Condor, 26: 31–32.
500. Gill, D. E., and W. E. Lanyon. 1965. Establishment, growth, and behavior of an extralimital population of house finches at Huntington, New York. Bird-Banding, 36: 1–14.
501. Gillespie, J. A. 1924. Some nestings of the crested flycatcher. Auk, 41: 41–44.
502. ———. 1927. Yellow-throated vireo breeding in Delaware Co., Pa. Auk, 44: 110–111.
503. Gillette, E. C. 1906. A bit of robin history. Bird-Lore, 8: 126–129.
504. Gilman, M. F. 1909. Nesting notes on the Lucy warbler. Condor, 11: 166–168.
505. Goddard, S. V., and V. V. Board. 1967. Reproductive success of red-winged blackbirds in north central Oklahoma. Wils. Bull., 79: 283–289.
506. Godwin, R. B. 1954. Nesting of the horned lark in the Atlanta area. Oriole, 19: 31–32.
507. Goff, M. 1932. A flycatcher history. Bird-Lore, 34: 191–195.
508. Goin, C. J., and O. B. Goin. 1954. Nest-building behavior of the Carolina wren. Wils. Bull., 66: 59.
509. Good, E. E. 1952. The life history of the American crow, *Corvus brachyrhynchos* Brehm. Dissert. Abstr., 17: 3133.
510. Goodell, F. C. 1940. Observations on the life history of the eastern kingbird. Mich. Biol. Sta., MS. *In* Kendeigh, 1952.
511. Goodge, W. R. 1959. Locomotion and other behavior of the dipper. Condor, 61: 4–17.
512. Goodpasture, A. V. 1908. A mockingbird's June. Bird-Lore, 10: 201–204.
513. Goodpasture, K. A. 1951. Cerulean warbler's nest in Nashville area. Migrant, 22: 32–33.
514. ———. 1953. Wood pewee builds with green leaves. Wils. Bull., 65: 117–118.
515. Goss, N. S. 1884. Notes on the nesting habits of the yellow-throated vireo (*Lanivireo flavifrons*). Auk, 1: 124–126.
516. ———. 1885. The black-capped vireo and nonpareil in southwestern Kansas. Auk, 2: 274–276.
517. Gould, P. J. 1961. Territorial relationships between cardinals and pyrrhuloxias. Condor, 63: 246–256.
518. Govan, A. C. 1948. Some wrens I have known. Bull. Mass. Aud. Soc., 32: 3–8.
519. Graber, J. W. 1961. Distribution, habitat requirements, and life history of the black-capped vireo (*Vireo atricapilla*). Ecol. Monog., 31: 313–336.
520. Graber, R., and J. Graber. 1951. Nesting of the parula warbler in Michigan. Wils. Bull., 63: 75–83.
521. Grady, M. M. 1943. An adaptable Carolina wren. Oriole, 8: 5–6.
522. Graham, Mrs. R. 1922. A devoted father. Ool., 39: 155.
523. Greulach, V. A. 1934. Notes on the nesting of the slate-colored junco. Auk, 51: 389–390.

524. GRIMES, S. A. 1928. The loggerhead shrike. Florida Nat., 1: 48–50.
525. ———. 1931. Notes on the orchard oriole. Florida Nat., 5: 1–7.
526. ———. 1932. Notes on the 1931 nesting season in the Jacksonville region—II. Florida Nat., 5: 57–63.
527. ———. 1935. The hooded warbler in Florida. Florida Nat., 8: 16–22.
528. ———. 1940. Scrub jay reminiscences. Bird-Lore, 42: 431–436.
529. ———. 1943. Notes from northeast Florida. Florida Nat., 16: 15–19.
530. ———. 1950. Cover photograph of male hooded warbler. Florida Nat., 23 (4).
531. GRIMM, W. C. 1941. Siskin nesting at Pymatuning. Cardinal, 5: 143.
532. GRINNELL, J. 1900a. Birds of the Kotzebue Sound region, Alaska. Pacific Coast Avif., 1: 1–80.
533. ———. 1900b. The varied thrush in summer. Condor, 2: 5–7.
534. ———. 1933. The LeConte thrashers of the San Joaquin. Condor, 35: 107–114.
535. GRINNELL, J., J. DIXON, AND J. M. LINSDALE. 1930. Vertebrate natural history of a section of northern California through the Lassen Peak region. Univ. Calif. Pub. Zool., 35: 1–594.
536. GRINNELL, J., AND J. M. LINSDALE. 1936. Vertebrate animals of Point Lobos Reserve, 1934–35. Carnegie Inst. Washington, Pub. 481: 1–159.
537. GRINNELL, J., AND T. I. STORER. 1924. Animal life in the Yosemite. Univ. of Calif. Press, Berkeley. 752 pp.
538. GRINNELL, L. I. 1943. Nesting habits of the common redpoll. Wils. Bull., 55: 155–163.
539. ———. 1944. Notes on breeding Lapland longspurs at Churchill, Manitoba. Auk, 61: 554–560.
540. GRISCOM, L. 1938. The birds of the Lake Umbagog region of Maine. Bull. Mus. Comp. Zool., Harvard, 66: 522–620.
541. GROPIUS, I. 1943. Bird panorama in a Lincoln garden. Bull. Mass. Aud. Soc., 27: 201–206.
542. ———. 1947. Queer bird behavior. Bull. Mass. Aud. Soc., 31: 235.
543. GROSS, A. O. 1921. The dickcissel (*Spiza americana*) of the Illinois prairies. Auk, 38: 1–26, 163–184.
544. ———. 1938. Nesting of the goldfinch. Bird-Lore, 40: 253–257.
545. ———. 1949. Nesting of the Mexican jay in the Santa Rita Mountains, Arizona. Condor, 51: 241–249.
546. GROSS, W. A. 1929. A cedar waxwing study in northern Michigan. Bird-Lore, 31: 178–182.
547. ———. 1932. Home-life of the American pipit. Bird-Lore, 34: 309–314.
548. ———. 1934. The warblers of the lilacs. Bird-Lore, 36: 158–162.
549. GROUT, M. K. 1945. A bird family idyl of the back yard. Bull. Mass. Aud. Soc., 29: 188.
550. GRUBB, D. B. 1909. Robin. Wils. Bull., 21: 43–44.
551. GUNDERSON, A. 1939. Nesting habits of the red-breasted nuthatch. Condor, 41: 259–260.
552. GUTHRIE, R. A. 1941. Notes from Woodward. Iowa Bird Life, 11: 14.
553. HACKETT, N. L. 1913. Notes on the breeding habits of *Agelaius phoeniceus*. Wils. Bull., 25: 36–37.
554. HAECKER, F. W. 1948. A nesting study of the mountain bluebird in Wyoming. Condor, 50: 216–219.
555. HALDEMAN, D. W. 1931. A study of the eastern song sparrow, *Melospiza melodia melodia*. Auk, 48: 385–406.
556. HALE, A. G. 1947. Housebuilding problems. Bull. Mass. Aud. Soc., 31: 236.
557. HALES, H. 1892. Bird notes of northern New Jersey. Ornith. and Ool., 17: 38–39.
558. ———. 1896. Peculiar traits of some scarlet tanagers. Auk, 13: 261–263.
559. HALL, G. A., AND N. LAITSCH. 1963. Brown creeper nesting in West Virginia. Wils. Bull., 75: 278–279.
560. HALL, MRS. J. W. 1924. Family life of Say phoebes and kingbirds. Ool., 41: 114.
561. HAMILTON, A., AND R. E. HAMILTON. 1954. Cowbird breeding at Dalton. Oriole, 19: 12.
562. HAMILTON, W. J., JR. 1943. Nesting of the eastern bluebird. Auk, 60: 91–94.
563. HANCOCK, J. L. 1911. Nature sketches in temperate America. A. C. McClurg and Co., Chicago. 451 pp.

564. HANN, H. W.   1937.   Life history of the ovenbird in southern Michigan. Wils. Bull., 49: 145–237.
565. ———.   1940.   Polyandry in the oven-bird. Wils. Bull., 52: 69–72.
566. ———.   1950.   Nesting behavior of the American dipper in Colorado. Condor, 52: 49–62.
567. HANNA, G. D.   1922.   The Aleutian rosy finch. Condor, 24: 88–91.
568. HANNA, W. C.   1931.   Odd nesting site of ash-throated flycatcher. Condor, 33: 216–217.
569. HARBAUM, F.   1921.   A family of wood thrushes. Bird-Lore, 23: 140–141.
570. HARDING, K. C.   1926.   Home life of the black-throated blue warbler. Bull. N. E. Bird-Banding Assoc., 2: 65–68.
571. ———.   1931.   Nesting habits of the black throated blue warbler. Auk, 48: 512–522.
572. HARDY, J. W.   1961.   Studies in behavior and phylogeny of certain New World jays (Garrulinae). Univ. Kansas Sci. Bull., 42: 13–149.
573. HARGRAVE, L. L.   1936.   Three broods of red-backed junco in one season. Condor, 38: 57–59.
574. HARLOW, R. C.   1908.   Nesting of the tufted tit in Pennsylvania. Ool., 25: 42–44.
575. ———.   1914.   Nesting of the worm-eating warbler in Hundington County, Pa. Ool., 31: 98–99.
576. ———.   1917.   Early nesting of the solitary vireo in Pennsylvania. Ool., 34: 165.
577. ———.   1922.   The breeding habits of the northern raven in Pennsylvania. Auk, 39: 399–410.
578. ———.   1951.   Tribal nesting of the pine siskin in Pennsylvania. Cassinia, 38: 4–9.
579. HARPER, F.   1958.   Birds of the Ungava Peninsula. Allen Press, Lawrence, Kansas. 171 pp.
580. HARPER, W. T.   1926.   A bluebird's nest. Bird-Lore, 28: 187–190.
581. HARRINGTON, A. B.   1923.   Observations on the mockingbird at Dallas, Texas. Bird-Lore, 25: 310–312.
582. HARRIS, R. B.   1956.   No vacancy. Bull. Mass. Aud. Soc., 40: 295–300.
583. HARRIS, R. D.   1933.   Observations on a nest of Sprague's pipit (*Anthus spraguei*). Can. Field Nat., 47: 91–95.
584. ———.   1944.   The chestnut-collared longspur in Manitoba. Wils. Bull., 56: 105–115.
585. HARRISON, H. H.   1950.   Cover photograph of male hooded warbler. Bull. Mass. Aud. Soc., 34(4).
586. ———.   1951.   Notes and observations on the Wilson's warbler. Wils. Bull., 63: 143–148.
587. HARRISON, W.   1890.   The prothonotary warbler. Ool., 7: 228–229.
588. HARTSHORNE, J. M.   1962.   Behavior of the eastern Bluebird at the nest. Living Bird, 1: 131–149.
589. HARVEY, G. F.   1903.   The diary of a cardinal's nest. Auk, 20: 54–57.
590. HAUSER, D. C.   1959.   Notes on pairing and nest-building of mismatched vireos. Wils. Bull., 71: 383–384.
591. HAVERSCHMIDT, F.   1952.   Nesting behavior of the southern house wren in Surinam. Condor, 54: 292–295.
592. HAWKINS, B.   1962.   Baltimore oriole breeding in Guilford County, North Carolina. Chat, 26: 101.
593. HAWKSLEY, O., AND A. P. McCORMACK.   1951.   Doubly-occupied nests of the eastern cardinal, *Richmondena cardinalis*. Auk, 68: 515–516.
594. HAYES, H. H.   1928.   Continuous mating of towhees. Wils. Bull., 40: 206.
595. HAYWARD, A. R., JR.   1892.   Among the "blue-grays." Ool., 9: 135–136.
596. HAYWARD, C. L.   1943.   Notes on the status of the red crossbill in Utah. Auk, 60: 276–278.
597. HEAD, A.   1903a.   Nesting of the ruby-crowned kinglet. Bird-Lore, 5: 52–54.
598. ———.   1903b.   Nesting habits of two flycatchers at Lake Tahoe. Bird-Lore, 5: 153–155.
599. ———.   1903c.   Louisiana tanager. Amer. Ornith., 3: 10–14.
600. ———.   1904.   Nesting habits of the black-headed grosbeak. Condor, 6: 35–37.
601. ———.   1906.   Observations on the notes and ways of two western vireos. Condor, 8: 149–150.
602. HEATH, H.   1920.   The nesting habits of the Alaska wren. Condor, 22: 49–55.
603. HEGNER, R. W.   1899.   Photographing a bluebird. Bird-Lore, 1: 43–44.

604. ———. 1909. Where does the male horned lark stay at night? Bird-Lore, 11: 75–76.
605. HEIL, C. E. 1909. The towhee. Bird-Lore, 11: 158–160.
606. HEINEMAN, L. D. 1955. Notes on robin nesting in Cass County. Nebraska Bird Review, 23: 12–15.
607. HELD, MRS. D. 1953. Nesting of the western blue grosbeak in Cherry County. Nebraska Bird Review, 21: 20.
608. HEMPEL, K. M. 1919. Notes on nesting bluebirds and house wrens. Bird-Lore, 21: 173–174.
609. HEMPHILL, F. A. 1941. Notes on white-breasted nuthatch. Ool., 58: 131–133.
610. HENDERSON, G. 1935. A blue-winged warbler record for Decatur County, Indiana. Wils. Bull., 47: 160–161.
611. HENDERSON, MRS. H. N. 1924. The phoebe. Bird-Lore, 26: 89–94.
612. HENDERSON, J. 1905. Colorado notes. Auk, 22: 421–422.
613. ———. 1907. Nesting of crossbills in Colorado. Auk, 24: 440–442.
614. ———. 1908. The American dipper in Colorado. Bird-Lore, 10: 1–7.
615. HENSHAW, H. W. 1875. Report upon geographic and geologic explorations and surveys west of 100th meridian. Vol. 5, ch. 3: 133–507. U. S. Gov't Printing Office, Washington.
616. HENSLEY, M. M. 1950. Notes on the breeding behavior of the Bell's vireo. Auk, 67: 243–244.
617. ———. 1959. Notes on the nesting of selected species of birds of the Sonoran Desert. Wils. Bull., 71: 86–92.
618. HERMAN, C. M. 1938. Sex ratios of banded eastern red-wings (Agelaius p. phoeniceus). Bird-Banding, 9: 92–93.
619. HERRICK, F. H. 1900. Care of nest and young. Auk, 17: 100–103.
620. ———. 1901. The home life of wild birds. G. P. Putnams Sons, New York. 148 pp. (revised ed., 1905.)
621. ———. 1902. The chebec's first brood. Bird-Lore, 4: 80–84.
622. ———. 1904. Red-eyed vireos, awake and asleep. Bird-Lore, 6: 113–116.
623. ———. 1935. Wild birds at home. D. Appleton-Century Co., New York. 345 pp.
624. HERSCHLER, I. M. 1919. Cardinals and wrens. Bird-Lore, 21: 246–247.
625. HERSEY, F. S. 1910. History of a double nest of the yellow warbler. Ool., 27: 69–70.
626. ———. 1933. Notes on tree swallows and bluebirds. Auk, 50: 109–110.
627. HESS, I. E. 1903. Loggerhead shrike. Amer. Ornith., 3: 147–150.
628. HEYDWEILLER, A. M. 1935. A comparison of winter and summer territories and seasonal variations of the tree sparrow (Spizella a. arborea). Bird-Banding, 6: 1–11.
629. ———. 1936. Private secretary to a sparrow. Bird-Lore, 38: 178–186.
630. HIEMENZ, N. M. 1944a. The blue-gray gnatcatcher near St. Cloud in 1944. Flicker, 16: 67–70.
631. ———. 1944b. The eastern ruby-crowned kinglet nesting in Minnesota. Flicker, 16: 80–81.
632. HICKS, L. E. 1933. The breeding birds of Ashtabula County, Ohio. Wils. Bull., 45: 168–195.
633. ———. 1934. Some additional Ohio breeding records. Wils. Bull., 46: 201–202.
634. ———. 1935. Distribution of breeding birds in Ohio. Ohio State Univ. Studies, Bull. 35, Vol. 6: 125–190.
635. HIGGINS, A. W. 1953. The Carolina wrens of Middleboro. Bull. Mass. Aud. Soc., 37: 339–340.
636. HIGGINS, H. 1941. Nesting notes on the cactus wren in southwestern Utah. Ool., 58: 117.
637. HIGMAN, H. W., AND E. J. LARRISON. 1951. Union Bay, the life of a city marsh. Univ. of Wash. Press, Seattle. 315 pp.
638. HINSCH, R. 1933. An oriole's nest. Bird-Lore, 35: 153–155.
639. HINTON, W. B. 1887. The purple martin in the South. Ornith. and Ool., 12: 77–78.
640. HODGES, L. A. 1926. Orchard oriole—a decade. Bull. Mass. Aud. Soc., 9: 12–13.
641. HODGSON, F. H. 1919. Two interesting observations. Bird-Lore, 21: 299–300.
642. HOFFMAN, E. 1958. A sparrow-wren puzzle. Pass. Pigeon, 20: 25–26.
643. HOFFMAN, LaV. 1943. An experience with house wrens. Jack-Pine Warb., 21: 65–66.
644. HOFFMAN, R. 1901. A chebec's second brood. Bird-Lore, 3: 160–162.
645. HOFSLUND, P. B. 1954. A life history of the yellowthroat, Geothlypis trichas. Ph.D. thesis, Univ. of Mich. Dissert. Abstr. #7664, Vol. 141: 741–742.

646. ———. 1956. The birds of Gooseberry Falls State Park. Flicker, 28: 62–65, 68–70.
647. HOFSTEAD, R. 1950. Bewick's wren nesting at Fort Snelling. Flicker, 22: 108.
648. HOLDEN, E. F. 1892. *Junco hyemalis* in eastern Massachusetts in June. Auk, 9: 72–73.
649. HOLMBERG, S. C. 1947. Blue-gray gnatcatcher nesting at Frontenac, Goodhue County. Flicker, 19: 55.
650. HOLT, E. G. 1921. Annotated list of the Avery bird collection in the Alabama Museum of Natural History. Mus. Paper #4, Ala. Mus. Nat. Hist. 142 pp.
651. HOLTZ, F. L. 1906. The rose-breasted grosbeak. Bird-Lore, 8: 161–164.
652. ———. 1907. The house wren. Bird-Lore, 9: 198–200.
653. HOPE, C. E. 1947. Nesting of the evening grosbeak in Algonquin Park, Ontario, 1946. Auk, 64: 463–464.
654. HORSFALL, R. B. 1924. Nesting of American crossbill in Multnomah County, Oregon. Murrelet, 5(2): 10.
655. HOSTETTER, D. R. 1961. Life history of the Carolina junco, *Junco hyemalis carolinensis* Brewster. Raven, 32: 97–170.
656. HOUCK, W. J., AND J. H. OLIVER. 1954. Unusual nesting behavior of the brown-headed nuthatch. Auk, 71: 330–331.
657. HOWE, R. H., JR. 1898. Breeding habits of the American robin *(Merula migratoria)* in eastern Massachusetts. Auk, 15: 162–167.
658. HOWELL, J. C. 1942. Notes on the nesting habits of the American robin *(Turdus migratorius* L.). Am. Midl. Nat., 28: 529–603.
659. HOWES, B. G. 1909. Of purple grackles *(Quiscalus quiscula)*. Ool., 26: 94.
660. HOWES, P. G. 1912. Bobolink data. Ool., 29: 269–275.
661. HOXIE, W. 1887. The boat-tailed grackle. Ornith. and Ool., 12: 165–166.
662. HOYT, J. S. Y. 1948. Observations on nesting associates. Auk, 65: 188–196.
663. HUBBARD, M. E. 1907. Bluebird tenants. Bird-Lore, 9: 11–15.
664. ———. 1909. A second season of bluebird tenants. Bird-Lore, 11: 63–70.
665. HUBER, R. L. 1960. Chestnut-collared longspurs in Clay County, Minnesota. Flicker, 32: 99–100.
666. HUEY, L. M. 1935. A pair of phainopeplas. Bird-Lore, 37: 401–404.
667. ———. 1936. Notes on the summer and fall birds of the White Mountains, Arizona. Wils. Bull., 48: 119–130.
668. HUNT, R. 1921. Nesting pine grosbeaks in Plumas County, California. Condor, 23: 187–190.
669. HUNTLEY, C. W. 1957. Keith County. Nebraska Bird Review, 25: 24–25.
670. HUTCHINS, J. 1902. The nesting of the yellow-throated vireo. Bird-Lore, 4: 120–123.
671. HYDE, A. S. 1939. The life history of Henslow's sparrow, *Passerherbulus henslowi* (Audubon). Univ. Mich. Mus. Zool. Misc. Publ., 41: 1–72.
672. ILLINGWORTH, J. F. 1901. The Bullock's and Arizona hooded orioles. Condor, 3: 98–100.
673. INGERSOLL, E. 1876. Our present knowledge of the nidification of the American kinglets. Bull. Nuttall Orn. Club, 1: 77–79.
674. IRVING, L. 1960. Birds of Anaktuvuk Pass, Kobuk, and Old Crow. U. S. Nat. Mus. Bull., 217: 1–409.
675. IVES, E. G. 1899. The cardinal at the Hub. Bird-Lore, 1: 83–87.
676. ———. 1902. A goldfinch idyl. Bird-Lore, 4: 148–150.
677. IVOR, H. R. 1944. Bird study and semi-captive birds: the rose-breasted grosbeak. Wils. Bull., 56: 91–104.
678. J., C. B. 1886. Notes from Red Wing, Minn. Ool., 3: 59.
679. JACKSON, MRS. R. E. 1941. Song sparrows assume role of foster parents. Bull. Mass. Aud. Soc., 25: 134–135.
680. JACOBS, D. 1946. First Minnesota nesting of the Philadelphia vireo. Flicker, 18: 57.
681. JACOBS, J. W. 1899. Nesting of the black-and-white warbler. Osprey, 3: 71–72.
682. ———. 1938. On the reasoning instinct of the tufted titmouse *(Baeolophus bicolor)*. Ool., 55: 6–7.
683. JAMISON, H. K. 1887. My experience with the breeding of the white-breasted nuthatch. Ornith. and Ool., 12: 189–190.
684. JAROSZ, J. A. 1952. A nesting study at Hayden's Lake, Hennepin County. Flicker, 24: 145–147.

685. JENSEN, J. K. 1930. Third nesting record of the Rocky Mountain evening grosbeak in New Mexico. Auk, 47: 568–570.
686. JETER, H. H. 1957. Eastern phoebe nesting in Louisiana. Wils. Bull., 69: 360–361.
687. JEWETT, F. B. 1899. Nesting observations on the black phoebe. Condor, 1: 13.
688. JEWETT, S. G. 1916. Nesting of the crossbill (Loxia curvirostra minor) in Crook Co., Oregon. Auk, 33: 201.
689. JEWETT, S. G., AND I. N. GABRIELSON. 1929. Birds of the Portland area, Oregon. Pacific Coast Avif., 19: 1–54.
690. JOHNSON, A. 1938. Nest building behavior in the loggerhead shrike group. Wils. Bull., 50: 246–248.
691. ———. 1940a. Bewick wren. 1940 Indiana Aud. Soc. Yearbook: 28–32.
692. ———. 1940b. Incubation behavior of Lanius ludovicianus in North Dakota. Wils. Bull., 52: 35–36.
693. JOHNSON, E. E. 1905. Contributions to the life history of the black-and-white warbler. Jour. Maine Ornith. Soc., 7: 39–41.
694. JOHNSON, D. H., M. D. BRYANT, AND A. H. MILLER. 1948. Vertebrate animals of the Providence Mountains area of California. Univ. of Calif. Pub. in Zool., 48: 221–376.
695. JOHNSON, H. 1901. (untitled). Amer. Ornith., 1: 124.
696. JOHNSON, H. C. 1900. In the breeding home of Clarke's nutcracker. Condor, 2: 49–52.
697. JOHNSON, H. H. 1921. The barn swallow. Ool., 38: 125–128.
698. JOHNSON, H. S. 1933. Notes on the family life of a pair of American pipits. Wils. Bull., 45: 114–117.
699. JOHNSON, N. K. 1963. Biosystematics of sibling species of flycatchers in the Empidonax hammondii–oberholseri–wrightii complex. Univ. Calif. Pub. Zool., 66: 79–238.
700. JOHNSON, R. E. 1965. Reproductive activities of rosy finches, with special reference to Montana. Auk, 82: 190–205.
701. JOHNSON, R. W. 1899. The home of a pair of wood thrushes. Osprey, 4: 17–18.
702. JOHNSTON, D. W. 1959. The incubation patch and related breeding data of crows. Murrelet, 40: 6–7.
703. JOHNSTON, MRS. H. C. 1934. The eastern Carolina wren nests again at Superior in 1934. Nebraska Bird Review, 2: 62.
704. JOHNSTON, R. F., and J. W. HARDY. 1962. Behavior of the purple martin. Wils. Bull., 74: 243–262.
705. JOHNSTONE, W. B. 1949. An annotated list of the birds of the East Kootenay, British Columbia. Occ. Papers B. C. Provincial Museum, 7: 1–87.
706. JONES, MRS. A. H. 1934. Some notes on thrushes. Nebraska Bird Review, 2: 65.
707. JONES, C. M. 1887. Nesting of the blue-headed vireo. Ornith. and Ool., 12: 26.
708. JONES, F. M. 1931. Nesting habits of the parula warbler. Migrant, 2: 20–21.
709. ———. 1936. Southwest Virginia nesting notes, 1936. Ool., 53: 85–90.
710. JONES, L. 1892. The prairie horned lark (Otocoris alpestris praticola). Wils. Bull., 4: 54–59.
711. ———. 1910. The birds of Cedar Point and vicinity. Wils. Bull., 22: 25–41, 97–115, 172–182.
712. ———. 1913. Some records of the feeding of nestlings. Wils. Bull., 25: 67–71.
713. JORDAN, A. A. 1901. My robin neighbors. Bird-Lore, 3: 108–109.
714. K., R. B. 1915. The rose-breasted grosbeak. Ool., 32: 209.
715. KALE, H. W., II. 1965. Ecology and bioenergetics of the long-billed marsh wren, Telmatodytes palustris griseus (Brewster), in Georgia salt marshes. Publ. Nuttall Orn. Club, 5: 1–142.
716. KAPP, C. L. 1905. Notes on a family of robins. Amer. Ornith., 5: 184–186.
718. KEESLER, R. L. 1921. Birds. Ool., 38: 170–171.
719. KEHRER, V., JR. 1940. Observations on the life history of the American redstart (Setophaga ruticilla). Mich. Biol. Sta., MS. In Kendeigh, 1952.
720. KELLOGG, C. E. 1919. Making friends with the golden-winged warbler. Bird-Lore, 21: 241–242.
721. KELLS, W. 1891. Nesting of the winter wren. Ornith. and Ool., 16: 139–140.
722. ———. 1892. Nest of the winter wren. Ornith. and Ool., 17: 154–155.
723. ———. 1902. Nesting of some Canadian warblers. Ottawa Nat., 15: 225–233.
724. KELLY, B. B. 1913. The building of a robin's nest. Bird-Lore, 15: 310–311.
725. KELSO, L. 1931. Some notes on young desert horned larks. Condor, 33: 60–65.

726. ———. 1939. The violet-green swallow at the nest. Ool., 56: 90–92.
727. KENDALL, J. B. 1941. Observations on nesting habits of the bluebird. Pass. Pigeon, 3: 63–65.
728. KENDEIGH, S. C. 1941a. Birds of a prairie community. Condor, 43: 165–174.
729. ———. 1941b. Territorial and mating behavior of the house wren. Illinois Biol. Monog., 3: 1–120.
730. ———. 1945. Nesting behavior of wood warblers. Wils. Bull., 57: 145–164.
731. ———. 1952. Parental care and its evolution in birds. Illinois Biol. Monog., 22: 1–356.
732. KENDEIGH, S. C., AND S. P. BALDWIN. 1937. Factors affecting yearly abundance of passerine birds. Ecol. Monog., 7: 92–123.
733. KENNARD, F. H. 1920. Notes on the breeding habits of the rusty blackbird in northern New England. Auk, 37: 412–422.
734. KENNARD, F. H., AND F. B. McKECHNIE. 1905. The breeding of the brown creeper in eastern Massachusetts. Auk, 22: 183–193.
735. KENT, F. W., AND R. F. VANE. 1958. Notes on the prothonotary warbler in Johnson County. Iowa Bird Life, 28: 51–53.
736. KERR, MRS. M. 1937. The cardinal. Blue Bird, 4: 94–95.
737. KESSEL, B., AND T. J. CADE. 1958. Birds of the Colville River, northern Alaska. Biol. Papers Univ. of Alaska, 2: 1–83.
738. KESSEL, B., AND G. B. SCHALLER. 1960. Birds of the Upper Sheenjek Valley, northeastern Alaska. Biol. Papers Univ. of Alaska, 4: 1–58.
739. KILGORE, W., AND W. J. BRECKENRIDGE. 1929. Connecticut warbler nesting in Minnesota. Auk, 46: 551–552.
740. KIMBALL, J. W. 1944. A fishy bird story. Auk, 61: 646–647.
741. KINGSBURY, E. W. 1933. The status and natural history of the bobolink (*Dolichonyx oryzivorus*, Linnaeus). Ph.D. thesis, Cornell Univ. Library, Ithaca, New York.
742. KINSEY, E. C. 1934. Notes on the sociology of the long-tailed yellow-breasted chat. Condor, 36: 235–237.
743. KIRK, MRS. M. R. 1935. A very modern Carolina wren. 1935 Indiana Aud. Soc. Yearbook: 63–65.
744. DE KIRILINE, L. 1948. Least flycatcher. Aud. Mag., 50: 149–153.
745. ———. 1951. Trials of a phoebe family. Aud. Mag., 53: 151–155.
746. ———. 1952. Red-breast makes a home. Aud. Mag., 54: 16–21.
747. ———. 1954. Irrepressible nuthatch. Aud. Mag., 56: 264–267.
748. KITCHIN, E. A. 1949. Birds of the Olympic Peninsula. Olympic Stationers, Port Angeles, Wash. 262 pp.
749. KLIMSTRA, W. D., AND W. O. STIEGLITZ. 1957. Notes on reproductive activities of robins in Iowa and Illinois. Wils. Bull., 69: 333–337.
750. KLUGH, A. B. 1921. Observations on the birds of Prince Edward Island. Can. Field Nat., 35: 58–59.
751. KNAPP, E. 1943. Life of the purple martin. Blue Bird, 10: 34.
752. KNIGHT, O. W. 1905. Contributions to the life history of the myrtle warbler. Jour. Maine Ornith. Soc., 7: 71–76.
753. ———. 1906a. Notes on the yellow palm warbler (*Dendroica palmarum hypochrysea*). Warbler, 2 (second series): 1–6.
754. ———. 1906b. Contributions to the life history of the Nashville warbler. Jour. Maine Ornith. Soc., 8: 8–11.
755. ———. 1907a. Contributions to the life history of the yellow warbler. Jour. Maine Ornith. Soc., 9: 6–9.
756. ———. 1907b. Contributions to the life history of the American redstart. Jour. Maine Ornith. Soc., 9: 33–35.
757. ———. 1908. The birds of Maine. C. H. Glass and Co., Bangor, Maine. 693 pp.
758. KNOWLES, E. H. M. 1938. Polygamy in the western lark sparrow. Auk, 55: 675–676.
759. KNOWLES, W. C. 1904. A bird that sang on its nest. Amer. Ornith., 4: 75–76.
760. KNOX, M. 1945. Crested flycatcher nestings. Migrant, 16: 8–9.
761. KOENIG, MRS. H. 1954. The nesting habits of our cardinals. Pass. Pigeon, 16: 56–58.
762. KOHLER, L. S. 1910. The American redstart. Ool., 27: 128.
763. ———. 1911a. Chestnut-sided warbler. Ool., 28: 91–92.
764. ———. 1911b. The rose-breasted grosbeak at Bloomfield, N. J. Ool., 28: 154–155.
765. ———. 1911c. The yellow warbler (*Dendroica aestiva aestiva*). Ool., 28: 116–117.

766. ———. 1911d. Breeding birds about Pompton Lake, Passaic Co., New Jersey. Ool., 28: 136–139.
767. ———. 1912. Hermit thrush in Passaic County, N. J. Wils. Bull., 24: 111–112.
768. ———. 1913a. The ovenbird. Ool., 30: 79–81.
769. ———. 1913b. Two unusual sets. Ool., 30: 120.
770. ———. 1914a. The black-and-white warbler. Ool., 31: 94–95.
771. ———. 1914b. The Maryland yellowthroat. Ool., 31: 111–114.
772. ———. 1914c. The yellow-breasted chat. Ool., 31: 115–116.
773. ———. 1915a. Home life of the scarlet tanager. Oriole [N. J.], 3: 4–8.
774. ———. 1915b. Cowbird's eggs. Ool., 32: 35–38.
775. ———. 1915c. The indigo bunting in northern New Jersey. Ool., 32: 77–78.
776. ———. 1916. Nesting of the Wilson warbler in New Jersey. Ool., 33: 104–106.
777. ———. 1923. Long-billed marsh wren. Ool., 40: 85–87.
778. ———. 1932a. Some nesting birds in Great Notch, N. J. Ool., 49: 40–41.
779. ———. 1932b. Experiences with a family of song sparrows during 1931. Ool., 49: 84.
780. KRAUSE, H. 1956. Orchard oriole in Otter Tail County. Flicker, 28: 127.
781. ———. 1965. Nesting of a pair of Canada warblers. Living Bird, 4: 5–11.
782. KUERZI, R. G. 1941. Life history studies of the tree swallow. Proc. Linn. Soc. N. Y., 52–53: 1–52.
783. L., D. E. 1884. The blue grosbeak, (*Guiraca caerulea*). Ornith. and Ool., 9: 19–20.
784. LACK, D. 1940. Courtship feeding in birds. Auk, 57: 169–178.
785. LACK, D., AND J. T. EMLEN, JR. 1939. Observations on breeding behavior in tricolored red-wings. Condor, 41: 225–230.
786. LACK, D., et al. 1941. Courtship feeding in birds. Auk, 58: 56–60.
787. LA FAVE, L. D. 1955. The unusual feeding of a young Nevada cowbird. Murrelet, 36: 25.
788. LA FORCE, E. F. 1939. The prothonotary warbler nests at Burlington. Iowa Bird Life, 9: 36–37.
789. LAKELA, O. 1942. Notes on the nesting barn swallows. Flicker, 14: 49.
790. LAMB, W. A. 1962. Clay-colored sparrow nesting in St. Clair County. Jack-Pine Warb., 40: 101.
791. LANGDON, R. M. 1933. The lark bunting. Bird-Lore, 35: 139–142.
792. LANGILLE, J. H. 1882. The hooded warbler in western New York. Bull. Nuttall Orn. Club, 7: 119–120.
793. LANYON, W. E. 1957. The comparative biology of the meadowlarks (*Sturnella*) in Wisconsin. Pub. Nuttall Orn. Club, 1: 1–67.
794. LA PARDE, W. H., JR. 1922. Nesting of Swainson's warbler in Atlanta. Ool., 39: 88–89.
795. LASKEY, A. R. 1935. Mockingbird life history studies. Auk, 52: 370–381.
796. ———. 1936. Fall and winter behavior of mockingbirds. Wils. Bull., 48: 241–255.
797. ———. 1939. A study of nesting eastern bluebirds. Bird-Banding, 10: 23–32.
798. ———. 1940. The 1939 nesting season of bluebirds at Nashville, Tennessee. Wils. Bull., 52: 183–190.
799. ———. 1944. A study of the cardinal in Tennessee. Wils. Bull., 56: 27–44.
800. ———. 1946a. A nine-year-old mockingbird and his mates. Bird-Banding, 17: 36–38.
801. ———. 1946b. Some Bewick wren nesting data. Migrant, 17: 39–43.
802. ———. 1947. Evidence of polyandry at a bluebird nest. Auk, 64: 314–315.
803. ———. 1948. Some nesting data on the Carolina wren at Nashville, Tennessee. Bird-Banding, 19: 101–121.
804. ———. 1950. A courting Carolina wren building over nestlings. Bird-Banding, 21: 1–6.
805. ———. 1957. Some tufted titmouse life history. Bird-Banding, 28: 135–145.
806. ———. 1958. Blue jays at Nashville, Tennessee. Movements, nesting, age. Bird-Banding, 29: 211–218.
807. LAUGHLIN, E. E. 1906. The Carolina wren. Amer. Ornith., 6: 128–130.
808. LAW, J. E. 1929. A query about a nest habit of the pine siskin. Wils. Bull., 41: 192.
809. LAWRENCE, L. DE K. 1947. Five days with a pair of nesting Canada jays. Can. Field Nat., 61: 1–11.

810. ———. 1948a. A white-throat trio and a warbler incident. Bird-Banding, 19: 122–123.

811. ———. 1948b. Comparative study of the nesting behavior of chestnut-sided and Nashville warblers. Auk, 65: 204–219.

812. ———. 1949. The red crossbills at Pimisi Bay, Ontario. Can. Field Nat., 63: 147–160.

813. ———. 1953a. Nesting life and behaviour of the red-eyed vireo. Can. Field Nat., 67: 47–77.

814. ———. 1953b. Notes on the nesting behavior of the Blackburnian warbler. Wils. Bull., 65: 135–144.

815. LAWRENCE, R. E. 1951. Photograph of male Kentucky warbler. Bull. Mass. Aud. Soc., 35: 283.

816. LEA, R. B. 1942. A study of the nesting habits of the cedar waxwing. Wils. Bull., 54: 225–237.

817. LEACH, L. D. 1909. Which shrike is it? Ool., 26: 215–216.

818. LEACH, R. W. 1927. My robin friends. Aud. Bull. (preceding Aud. Ann. Bull.), 18: 53.

819. LEHRKE, MRS. G. W. 1947. Cedar waxwing dismantles robin's nest. Flicker, 19: 24–25.

820. LEISTER, C. W. 1918. A scene from the home-life of the chestnut-sided warbler. Bird-Lore, 20: 297–298.

821. LELAND, H. J. 1899. Nesting of the western flycatcher in San Gabriel Canon. Condor, 1: 82.

822. LEVY, F. 1920. An unusual horned lark family. Bird-Lore, 22: 85–86.

823. LEWIS, H. F. 1921. A nesting of the Philadelphia vireo. Auk, 38: 26–44, 185–202.

824. LEWIS, J. G. 1923. Notebook notes. Ool., 40: 133.

825. LIGON, J. S. 1961. New Mexico birds and where to find them. Univ. of New Mexico Press, Albuquerque. 360 pp.

826. LILLIE, H. C. 1891. House finch. Ool., 8: 30–31.

827. LINSDALE, J. M. 1928a. Variations in the fox sparrow (*Passerella iliaca*) with reference to natural history and osteology. Univ. Calif. Pub. Zool., 30: 251–392.

828. ———. 1928b. Birds of a limited area in eastern Kansas. Univ. of Kansas Sci. Bull., 18: 517–626.

829. ———. 1937. The natural history of magpies. Pacific Coast Avif., 25: 1–234.

830. ———. 1938. Environmental responses of vertebrates in the Great Basin. Am. Mid. Nat., 19: 1–206.

831. ———. 1950. Observations on the Lawrence goldfinch. Condor, 52: 255–259.

832. ———. 1957. Goldfinches on the Hastings Natural History Reservation. Am. Mid. Nat., 57: 1–119.

833. LINTON, C. B. 1911. Unusual nesting site of the San Nicholas rock wren. Condor, 13: 109.

834. LIPPINCOTT, J. W. 1913. Barn swallows in springtime. Bird-Lore, 15: 161–164.

835. LITSEY, J. B., JR. 1911. Scissor-tailed flycatcher (*Milvulus forficatus*). Ool., 28: 106–107.

836. LITTLEFIELD, M. J., AND F. LEMKAU. 1928. History of a cedar waxwing family. Bull. N. E. Bird-Banding Assoc., 4: 85–89.

837. LOGAN, S. 1951. Cardinal, *Richmondena cardinalis*, assists in feeding of robins. Auk, 68: 516–517.

838. LONG, H. V. 1917. Birds of Cohasset Island. Bull. Mass. Aud. Soc., 2: 5–8.

839. LONG, MRS. M. T. 1934–35. My cardinal family. Aud. Ann. Bull., 24–25: 68.

840. LONGLEY, W. 1944. Breeding bird census in Idaho. Flicker, 16: 51–54.

841. LONGSTREET, R. J. 1937. Acadian flycatchers at home. Florida Nat., 10: 83–87.

842. LORD, F. P. 1954. Nesting of a pine siskin. New Hampshire Bird News, 7(3): 32.

843. LORING, A. 1890. Notes on the birds of Tioga Co., N. Y. Ornith. and Ool., 15: 81–87.

844. LOUCKS, W. E. 1895. The life history and distribution of the prothonotary warbler in Illinois. Bull. Illinois Nat. Hist. Survey, 4: 10–35.

845. ———. 1898. Life history of the prothonotary warbler. Part 2, the nest; Part 3, no subtitle. Osprey, 2: 111–113, 129–131.

846. LOUND, M., AND R. LOUND. 1960. A boreal chickadee nest in forest country. Pass. Pigeon, 22(1): 31–32.

847. LOVELAND, L. S. 1953. Five years of phoebe housekeeping. Bull. Mass. Aud. Soc., 37: 403–405.

848. LOVELL, H. B.   1943.   The nest of a Kentucky warbler. Kentucky Warb., 19: 51–52.
849. ————.   1944.   Breeding records of the prairie horned lark in Kentucky. Auk, 61: 648–650.
850. ————.   1950.   Observations of nesting activities of the redstart. Bull. Maine Aud. Soc., 6: 49–50.
851. LOVELL, H. B., AND A. L. STAMM.   1948.   Breeding of the cedar waxwing in Kentucky. Auk, 65: 461–462.
852. LOW, S. H.   1933.   Further notes on the nesting of tree swallows. Bird-Banding, 4: 76–87.
853. ————.   1934.   Nest distribution and survival ratio of tree swallows. Bird-Banding, 5: 24–30.
854. LUMLEY, E.   1933.   Late nesting in 1932. Murrelet, 14: 17–18.
855. LUNK, W. A.   1962.   The rough-winged swallow, *Stelgidopteryx ruficollis* (Vieillot). Pub. Nuttall Ornith. Club, 4: 1–155.
856. LUSK, R. D.   1901.   In the summer home of the buff-breasted flycatcher. Condor, 3: 38–41.
857. McCABE, R. A.   1961.   The selection of colored nest boxes by house wrens. Condor, 63: 322–329.
858. ————.   1963.   Renesting of the alder flycatcher. Proc. XIII Intern. Ornith. Congress: 319–328.
859. ————.   1965.   Nest construction by house wrens. Condor, 67: 229–234.
860. McCLANAHAN, R. C.   1935.   A study of a robin nest. MS. *In* Howell, 1942.
861. McCLINTOCK, N.   1909.   A successful failure. Bird-Lore, 11: 198–204.
862. ————.   1910.   A hermit thrush study. Auk, 27: 409–418.
863. ————.   1933.   Ligonier bird notes. Cardinal, 3: 125–129.
864. McGEEVER, M. S.   1914.   A redstart record. Ool., 31: 153–154.
865. McGREGOR, R. C.   1897.   Birds of Estes Park. Nidol., 4: 38–39.
866. McGREW, A. D.   1918.   Observations on a family of winter wrens. Ool., 35: 162–164.
867. McILHENNY, E. A.   1937.   Life history of the boat-tailed grackle in Louisiana. Auk, 54: 274–295.
868. McLAUGHLIN, R. B.   1887.   Nesting of the pine-creeping warbler. Ornith. and Ool., 12: 171.
869. ————.   1888.   Nesting of the mountain solitary vireo. Ornith. and Ool., 13: 113–114.
870. McMILLEN, H. W.   1909.   The prothonotary warbler. Ool., 26: 102–105.
871. MacDONALD, M.   1947.   The birds of Brewery Creek. Oxford Univ. Press, London, Toronto, New York. 334 pp.
872. MACGILLIVRAY, H. D.   1965.   Breeding of the mockingbird, *Mimus polyglottos*, in Newfoundland. Can. Field Nat., 79: 209–211.
873. MACK, E. T.   1885.   White-bellied nuthatch. Young Ool., 1: 142–143.
874. MACKLIN, T.   1917.   Our neighbors of the grape-vine. Bird-Lore, 19: 127–131.
875. MacLOGHLIN, A. E.   1932.   Evening grosbeak seen feeding its young in Muskoka. Can. Field Nat., 46: 68.
876. MacQUEEN, P. M.   1950.   Territory and song in the least flycatcher. Wils. Bull., 62: 194–205.
877. MAHAWALD, MR. AND MRS. A.   1943.   Observations on goldfinches. Flicker, 15: 52.
878. MAILLIARD, J. W.   1921.   Notes on the nesting of the Yosemite fox sparrow, calliope hummingbird and western wood pewee at Lake Tahoe, California. Condor, 23: 73–77.
879. MAILLIARD, J.   1930.   Happenings in a robin household. Condor, 32: 77–80.
880. MALTBY, F.   1931.   In the nesting haunts of the western winter wren. Ool., 48: 2–6.
881. ————.   1935.   Western golden-crowned kinglet. Ool., 52: 130–132.
882. MARSH, C. H.   1885.   Notes from Silver City, N. M. Ornith. and Ool., 10: 147–149, 163–165.
883. MARSHALL, L. F.   1918.   A tragedy. Bird-Lore, 20: 338–340.
884. MARTIN, D.   1918.   The bobolink. Ool., 35: 158.
885. MARTIN, E. P.   1945.   Ups and downs of the wrens. Bull. Mass. Aud. Soc., 29: 213–214.
886. MARTIN, J.   1909.   A devoted parent. Bird-Lore, 11: 129.
887. MASON, R. F.   1952.   Yellow-throated vireo breeding near Lockhart. Florida Nat., 25: 83.

888. MAXON, W. R. 1902. Notes on some yellow-throated vireos' nests. Osprey, 1 (new series): 37–39.

889. MAYFIELD, H. 1960. The Kirtland's warbler. Cranbrook Institute of Sci., Bloomfield Hills, Mich. 242 pp.

890. ———. 1964. Yearly fluctuations in a population of purple martins. Auk, 81: 274–280.

891. MAYNARD, C. J. 1905. The warblers of New England. C. J. Maynard, West Newton, Mass. 138 pp.

892. MAYR, E. 1941. Redwing observations of 1940. Proc. Linn. Soc. N. Y., 1940–1941: 75–83.

893. MEANLEY, B. 1959. Notes on Bachman's sparrow in central Louisiana. Auk, 76: 232–234.

894. MEARNS, E. A. 1886. Some birds of Arizona. Auk, 3: 289–307.

895. MENDALL, H. L. 1937. Nesting of the bay-breasted warbler. Auk, 54: 429–439.

896. MERCER, B. 1905. Our 'pioneer tenants.' Bird-Lore, 7: 174–176.

897. MERRIAM, F. A. 1890. Was he a philanthropist? Auk, 7: 404–407.

898. ———. 1896a. Nesting habits of *Phainopepla nitens* in California. Auk, 13: 38–43.

899. ———. 1896b. Notes on some of the birds of southern California. Auk, 13: 115–124.

900. MERRIAM, H. F. 1917. Nesting of the Cape May warbler at Lake Edward, Quebec. Auk, 34: 410–413.

901. MERRILL, J. C. 1888. Notes on the birds of Fort Klamath, Oregon. Auk, 5: 357–366.

902. ———. 1898. Notes on the birds of Fort Sherman, Idaho. Auk, 15: 14–22.

903. MERRILL, J. P. 1878. Notes on the ornithology of southern Texas. Proc. U. S. Nat. Mus., 1: 118–173.

904. MERRITT, E. R. 1943. A curious building site. Bull. Mass. Aud. Soc., 27: 98.

905. MERRITT, M. 1916. Wren notes. Wils. Bull., 28: 92–94.

906. MEWALDT, L. R. 1952. The incubation patch of the Clark nutcracker. Condor, 54: 361.

907. ———. 1956. Nesting behavior of the Clark nutcracker. Condor, 58: 3–23.

908. MEYER, H., AND R. R. NEVIUS. 1943. Some observations on the nesting and development of the prothonotary warbler, *Protonotaria citrea*. Migrant, 14: 31–36.

909. MEYER, I. R. 1913. Some observations of a pair of brown creepers (*Certhia familiaris americana*). Auk, 30: 587–589.

910. MICHAEL, C. W. 1934. Nesting of the red-breasted nuthatch. Condor, 36: 113.

911. MICHENER, H. 1925. Polygamy practiced by the house finch. Condor, 27: 116.

912. MICHENER, H., AND J. R. MICHENER. 1945. California jays, their storage and recovery of food, and observations at one nest. Condor, 47: 206–210.

913. MICKEY, F. W. 1943. Breeding habits of McCown's longspur. Auk, 60: 181–209.

914. MIDDLETON, D. S. 1961. The summering warblers of Crawford County, Michigan. Jack-Pine Warb., 39: 34–50.

915. MIDDLETON, M. P. 1943. Some observations of the loggerhead shrike in Lincoln County. Nebraska Bird Review, 11: 1–4.

916. ———. 1947. Notes on the nesting of the blue grosbeak. Nebraska Bird Review, 15: 8–10.

917. MIDDLETON, R. J. 1929. Notes from Norristown, Pennsylvania. Bull. N. E. Bird-Banding Assoc., 5: 62–65.

918. ———. 1936. A pair of northern crested flycatchers (*Myiarchus crinitus boreus*) mated for three consecutive years. Bird-Banding, 7: 171–172.

919. MILLER, A. B. 1943. Four-brooded cardinals. Cardinal, 6: 21–22.

920. MILLER, A. H. 1931. Systematic revision and natural history of the American shrikes (*Lanius*). Univ. Calif. Pub. Zool., 38: 11–242.

921. ———. 1937. A comparison of behavior of certain North American and European shrikes. Condor, 39: 119–122.

922. MILLER, E. V. 1941. Behavior of the Bewick wren. Condor, 43: 81–99.

923. MILLER, F. W. 1925. The nest and eggs of the black rosy finch. Condor, 27: 3–7.

924. MILLER, L. DE V. 1921. The chestnut-sided warbler. Ool., 38: 154.

925. MILLER, L. 1926. Nests of the scarlet tanager. Ool., 43: 149.

926. ———. 1929. Bobolinks. Ool., 46: 9–10.

927. ———. 1930. Bobolink, 1929. Ool., 47: 156–157.

928. MILLER, M. M. 1902. The warbling vireo, a nest singer. Bird-Lore, 4: 161–162.

929. MILLER, N. 1916. The chipping sparrow. Bird-Lore, 18: 151–155.

930. MILLER, R. F. 1906. Long-billed marsh wren (*Telmatodytes palustris*) in Phila-delphia County, Penn. Ool., 23: 117–124.

931. ———. 1928. Nesting of the white-breasted nuthatch in Center County, Pa. Ool., 45: 134–138.

932. MILLS, E. A. 1931. Bird memories of the Rockies. Riverside Press, Cambridge, Mass. 263 pp.

933. MITCHELL, W. I. 1898. Nesting of the American dipper. Ool., 15: 64.

934. MOESEL, J. 1916. A domestic tragedy. Bird-Lore, 18: 160–163.

935. MOFFETT, B. 1885. Rose-breasted grosbeak. Young Ool., 2: 47.

936. MOODY, C. S. 1904. My favorite bird. Amer. Ornith., 4: 284–286.

937. MOORE, G. E. 1942. Meramec bird notes. Blue Bird, 9: 41–42.

938. ———. 1944. Parula nest described. Blue Bird, 11: 47.

939. MOORE, H. 1938–41. Note on nesting robins. Cassinia, 31: 40.

940. MOORE, L. 1936. Notes on nesting birds of Papilio Forest. Florida Nat., 10: 18–19.

941. ———. 1937. The Florida wrens. Florida Nat., 10: 35–38.

942. MOORE, M., AND D. MOORE. 1940. Nesting of a ruby-crowned kinglet at Redlands, California. Condor, 42: 263.

943. MOORE, W. H. 1904. Notes concerning New Brunswick warblers. Ottawa Nat., 18: 97–103.

944. ———. 1905. The red-breasted nuthatch (*Sitta canadensis*). Ottawa Nat., 19: 139–141.

945. ———. 1906. The red-breasted nuthatch. Ool., 23: 153–154.

946. ———. 1908. Blue birds of the Maritime Provinces. Ottawa Nat., 22: 174–179.

947. MORRELL, C. H. 1898. Nesting habits of the red-breasted nuthatch. Ool., 15: 55–56.

948. ———. 1899. Some winter birds of Nova Scotia. Auk, 16: 250–253.

949. MORRIS, P. 1900. Notes on the yellow warbler. Ool., 17: 12.

950. MORRISON, G. G. 1891. A rose-breasted grosbeak widower. Ool., 8: 186–187.

951. MORSE, E. M. 1923a. The history of a black-capped chickadee family. Bird-Lore, 25: 187–188.

952. ———. 1923b. A summer with a catbird family. Bird-Lore, 25: 251–252.

953. MOSELEY, E. L. 1936. Pugnacious cardinals. Wils. Bull., 48: 312.

954. MOSELEY, M. 1920. Highland Park. Aud. Bull., 7: 39–41.

955. MOUNTS, B. T. 1922. A blue-gray gnatcatcher's nest. Wils. Bull., 34: 116–117.

956. MOUSLEY, H. 1916a. Five years personal notes and observations on the birds of Hatley, Stanstead County, Quebec—1911–1915. Auk, 33: 57–73, 168–186.

957. ———. 1916b. The breeding of the prairie horned lark at Hatley, Stanstead County, Quebec. Auk, 33: 281–286.

958. ———. 1918. Further notes and observations on the birds of Hatley, Stanstead County, Quebec, 1916–1917. Auk, 35: 289–310.

959. ———. 1924. A study of the home life of the northern parula and other warblers at Hatley, Stanstead County, Quebec, 1921–1922. Auk, 41: 263–288.

960. ———. 1926. A further study of the home life of the northern parula, and of the yellow warbler and ovenbird. Auk, 43: 184–197.

961. ———. 1928. Notes on the birds, orchids, ferns and butterflies of the Province of Quebec, 1927. Can. Field Nat., 42: 25–29.

962. ———. 1930a. The home life of the American goldfinch. Can. Field Nat., 44: 177–179.

963. ———. 1930b. A further study of the home life of the American goldfinch. Can. Field Nat., 44: 204–207.

964. ———. 1932. A third study of the home life of the eastern goldfinch (*Spinus tristis tristis*). Can. Field Nat., 46: 200–203.

965. ———. 1933. A study of the home-life of the northern yellow-throat (*Geothlypis trichas brachiodactyla*). Can. Field Nat., 47: 6–10.

966. ———. 1934a. A study of the home life of the northern crested flycatcher (*Myiarchus crinitus boreus*). Auk, 51: 207–216.

967. ———. 1934b. A study of the home life of the short-billed marsh wren (*Cistothorus stellaris*). Auk, 51: 439–445.

968. ———. 1935. Is the eastern goldfinch, *Spinus tristis tristis*, double-brooded? A fourth study of its home life. Can. Field Nat., 49: 145–147.

969. ———. 1937. A study of the eastern song sparrow (*Melospiza melodia melodia*). Aud. Ann. Bull., 27: 24–26.

970. MUIRHEAD, P. 1942. Least flycatcher. Mich. Biol. Sta., MS. *In* Kendeigh, 1952.
971. MUMFORD, R. E. 1952. Bell's vireo in Indiana. Wils. Bull., 64: 224–233.
972. ———. 1954. Brewer's blackbird nesting in Indiana. Wils. Bull., 66: 61–62.
973. ———. 1964. The breeding biology of the Acadian flycatcher. Misc. Pub. Mus. Zool., Univ. of Mich., 125: 1–50.
974. MUNRO, J. A. 1922. A proposed bird sanctuary in British Columbia. Can. Field Nat., 36: 26–30.
975. ———. 1949. The birds and mammals of the Vanderhoof Region, British Columbia. Am. Mid. Nat., 41: 1–138.
976. MURIE, A. 1946. Observations on the birds of Mount McKinley National Park, Alaska. Condor, 48: 253–261.
977. ———. 1956. Nesting records of the Arctic willow warbler in Mount McKinley National Park, Alaska. Condor, 58: 292–293.
978. MURPHY, R. C. 1911. The breeding of the pine warbler in Rhode Island. Bird-Lore, 13: 187–190.
979. MURRAY, J. J. 1934. The blue-gray gnatcatcher moving its nest. Wils. Bull., 46: 128.
980. ———. 1949. Nesting habits of the raven in Rockbridge County. Raven, 20: 40–43.
981. MYERS, H. W. 1907a. Nesting ways of the western gnatcatcher. Condor, 9: 48–51.
982. ———. 1907b. Nesting habits of *Phainopepla nitens*. Condor, 9: 101–103.
983. ———. 1908. Observations on the nesting habits of the phainopepla. Condor, 10: 72–75.
984. ———. 1909a. Notes on the habits of *Phainopepla nitens*. Condor, 11: 22–23.
985. ———. 1909b. Nesting habits of the rufous-crowned sparrow. Condor, 11: 131–134.
986. ———. 1909c. The hanging home in the oak tree. Bird-Lore, 11: 209–212.
987. ———. 1911. Nesting habits of the western flycatcher. Condor, 13: 87–89.
988. MYERS, J. A. 1909. Wood thrush. Wils. Bull., 21: 42–43.
989. NAUMAN, E. D. 1930a. The mockingbird breeds in Iowa. Wils. Bull., 42: 57–59.
990. ———. 1930b. The nesting habits of the Baltimore oriole. Wils. Bull., 42: 295–296.
991. NELSON, F. A. 1932. A martin colony. Bull. Mass. Aud. Soc., 16(5): 5–6.
992. NELSON, M. H. 1965. Barn swallow observations. Pass. Pigeon, 27: 131–138.
993. NERO, R. W. 1956. A behavior study of the redwinged blackbird. I. Mating and nesting activities. II. Territoriality. Wils. Bull., 68: 5–37, 129–150.
994. ———. 1963. Comparative behavior of the yellow-headed blackbird, red-winged blackbird, and other Icterids. Wils. Bull., 75: 376–413.
995. NEWBERRY, W. C. 1916. A chapter in the life history of the wren-tit. Condor, 18: 65–68.
996. NEWMAN, D. L. 1958. A nesting of the Acadian flycatcher. Wils. Bull., 70: 130–144.
997. NICE, M. M. 1926a. Behavior of blackburnian, myrtle, and black-throated blue warblers, with young. Wils. Bull., 38: 82–83.
998. ———. 1926b. A study of a nesting of magnolia warbler (*Dendroica magnolia*). Wils. Bull., 38: 185–199.
999. ———. 1928. Magnolia warblers in Pelham, Massachusetts, in 1928. Wils. Bull., 40: 252–253.
1000. ———. 1929. The fortunes of a pair of Bell vireos. Condor, 31: 13–18.
1001. ———. 1930a. Do birds usually change mates for the second brood? Bird-Banding, 1: 70–72.
1002. ———. 1930b. Observations at a nest of myrtle warblers. Wils. Bull., 42: 60–61.
1003. ———. 1930c. Experiences with song sparrows in 1929. Wils. Bull., 42: 219–220.
1004. ———. 1930d. A study of a nesting of black-throated blue warblers. Auk, 47: 338–345.
1005. ———. 1930e. Five song sparrows raised with a cowbird. Auk, 47: 419–420.
1006. ———. 1931a. The birds of Oklahoma. Pub. No. 3, Univ. of Oklahoma Biol. Survey. 224 pp.
1007. ———. 1931b. Five little migrant shrikes. Wils. Bull., 43: 149–150.
1008. ———. 1931c. A study of two nests of the ovenbird. Auk, 48: 215–228.
1009. ———. 1932a. Observations on the nesting of the blue-gray gnatcatcher. Condor, 34: 18–22.
1010. ———. 1932b. The song sparrow breeding season of 1931. Bird-Banding, 3: 45–50.
1011. ———. 1933. Relations between the sexes in song sparrows. Wils. Bull., 45: 51–59.

1012. ———. 1936a. The way of a song sparrow. Bird-Lore, 38: 257–264.
1013. ———. 1936b. The nest in the rose hedge. Bird-Lore, 38: 337–343.
1014. ———. 1937. Studies in the life history of the song sparrow, I. Trans. Linn. Soc. of New York, 4: 1–247.
1015. ———. 1938a. A famous song sparrow and his eleven wives. Aud. Ann. Bull., 28: 5–7.
1016. ———. 1938b. Territory and mating with the song sparrow. Proc. VIII Intern. Ornith. Cong.: 324–338.
1017. ———. 1939a. The watcher at the nest. Macmillan Co., N. Y. 159 pp.
1018. ———. 1939b. "Territorial song" and non-territorial behavior of goldfinches in Ohio. Wils. Bull., 51: 123.
1019. ———. 1943. Studies in the life history of the song sparrow, II. Trans. Linn. Soc. of New York, 6: 1–328.
1020. NICE, M. M., AND L. B. NICE. 1932. A study of two nests of the black-throated green warbler. Bird-Banding, 3: 95–105, 157–172.
1021. NICE, M. M., AND R. H. THOMAS. 1948. A nesting of the Carolina wren. Wils. Bull., 60: 139–158.
1022. NICE, M. M., AND N. E. COLLIAS. 1961. A nesting of the least flycatcher. Auk, 78: 145–149.
1023. NICHOLS, N. 1948. Peeper pond. Bull. Mass. Aud. Soc., 32: 95–97, 173–177.
1025. NICHOLSON, D. J. 1929. Nesting of the yellow-throated warbler in Volusia County, Florida. Wils. Bull., 41: 45–46.
1026. ———. 1936. Observations on the Florida blue jay. Wils. Bull., 48: 26–33.
1027. NICHOLSON, E. M. 1930. Field notes on Greenland birds. Ibis, 6: 280–313.
1028. NICKELL, W. P. 1942. The nesting of the willow thrush in Charlevoix County, Michigan. Jack-Pine Warb., 20: 99–108.
1029. ———. 1949. A large nest of the rough-winged swallow. Wils. Bull., 61: 188–189.
1030. ———. 1954. Red-wings hatch and raise a yellow-billed cuckoo. Wils. Bull., 66: 137–138.
1031. ———. 1956. Nesting of the black-capped chickadee in the southern peninsula of Michigan. Jack-Pine Warb., 34: 127–138.
1032. ———. 1964a. Brown-headed cowbird fledged in barn swallow nest. Wils. Bull., 76: 94.
1033. ———. 1964b. Brown-headed cowbird fledged in nest of black-throated blue warbler. Wils. Bull., 76: 96.
1034. NOLAN, V., JR. 1958. Anticipatory food-bringing in the prairie warbler. Auk, 75: 263–278.
1035. ———. 1960. Breeding behavior of the Bell vireo in southern Indiana. Condor, 62: 225–244.
1036. ———. 1963. An analysis of the sexual nexus in the prairie warbler. Proc. XIII Intern. Ornith. Congress: 329–337.
1037. ———. 1965. A male cardinal helper at a nest of yellow-breasted chats. Wils. Bull., 77: 196.
1038. NORRIS, J. P. 1886. Nests of the long-billed marsh wren. Ornith. and Ool., 11: 36.
1039. NORRIS, R. 1942. Notes on the nesting of a pair of Alabama towhees. Oriole, 7: 14–17.
1040. NORRIS, R. A. 1958. Comparative biosystematics and life history of the nuthatches Sitta pygmaea and Sitta pusilla. Univ. Calif. Pub. Zool., 56: 119–300.
1041. NORWOOD, J., AND R. NORWOOD. 1956. Nesting observations of brown-headed nuthatches. Chat, 20: 73–74.
1042. NORWOOD, J. R. 1961. Prothonotary warbler breeding in Mecklenburg County, North Carolina. Chat, 25: 70.
1043. NYE, H. A. 1929. Juncos nesting. Bull. Mass. Aud. Soc., 13(4): 6.
1044. OBERHOLSER, H. C. 1927. Our friend the cardinal. Cardinal, 2: 1–5.
1045. ———. 1938. The bird life of Louisiana. Bull. Dept. of Conservation, State of Louisiana, 28: 1–834.
1046. OBERLANDER, G. 1939. The history of a family of black phoebes. Condor, 41: 133–151.
1047. ODUM, E. P. 1931. Notes on the nesting habits of the hooded warbler. Wils. Bull., 43: 316–317.
1048. ———. 1941a. Annual cycle of the black-capped chickadee, 1. Auk, 58: 314–333.
1049. ———. 1941b. Annual cycle of the black-capped chickadee, 2. Auk, 58: 518–535.
1050. ———. 1942. Long incubation by a Carolina chickadee. Auk, 59: 430–431.

1051. ———. 1945. A nest of the blackburnian warbler in Pickens County, Georgia. Oriole, 10: 53.
1052. ———. 1948. Nesting of the mountain vireo at Athens, Georgia, conclusive evidence of a southward invasion. Oriole, 13: 17–20.
1053. ODUM, E. P., AND D. W. JOHNSTON. 1951. The house wren breeding in Georgia: An analysis of a range extension. Auk, 68: 357–366.
1054. OLIVER, J. H., JR. 1952. Unusual nesting behavior of the brown-headed nuthatch. Oriole, 17: 17.
1055. ORFORD, W. McL. 1929. Cardinal vs. catbird. Bird-Lore, 31: 263.
1056. ORIANS, G. H. 1960. Autumnal breeding in the tricolored blackbird. Auk, 77: 379–398.
1057. ———. 1961a. The ecology of blackbird (Agelaius) social systems. Ecol. Monog., 31: 285–312.
1058. ———. 1961b. Social stimulation within blackbird colonies. Condor, 63: 330–337.
1059. ORIANS, G. H., AND G. COLLIER. 1963. Competition and blackbird social systems. Evol., 17: 449–459.
1060. ORMSBEE, C. O. 1894. Notes on the phoebe. Ool., 11: 285–287.
1061. ORR, R. T. 1942. A study of the birds of the Big Basin Region of California. Am. Mid. Nat., 27: 273–337.
1062. ———. 1951. Observations on the birds of northeastern Idaho. Proc. Cal. Acad. Sci., fourth series, 27: 1–16.
1063. OSGOOD, W. H. 1892. The Californian bush-tit. Ool., 9: 227–228.
1064. OSTERHOUT, G. E. 1918. Notes on the house finch, Carpodacus mexicanus frontalis (Say). Ool., 35: 57.
1065. OTTO, M. C. 1919. To hatch and to raise. Bird-Lore, 21: 179–180.
1066. OWEN, D. E. 1899. A family of nestlings. Auk, 16: 221–225.
1067. PAFF, W. A. 1930. The blue-wings. Bird-Lore, 32: 343–346.
1068. ———. 1933. When Brewster's warbler breeds. Bird-Lore, 35: 145–147.
1069. PAINTER, R. H. 1950. Cowbird vs. bluebird. Blue Bird, 17(9): 1–2.
1070. PALMER, R. S. 1949. Maine birds. Bull. Mus. Comp. Zool., Harvard Univ., 102: 1–656.
1071. PALMER, W. 1901. The blue-gray gnatcatcher. Osprey, 5: 86–88.
1072. PARKER, H. G. 1886. The history of a bird box. Ool., 3: 31–32.
1073. PARKES, K. C. 1953. The incubation patch in males of the suborder Tyranni. Condor, 55: 218–219.
1074. PARKS, G. H. 1941. Junco jottings. Ool., 58: 38–41.
1075. ———. 1949. Junco family's interrelations reveal further complications. Bird-Banding, 20: 50.
1076. PARMALEE, E. W. 1926. The tale of two robins. Bird-Lore, 28: 338.
1077. PARMELEE, D. F. 1959. The breeding behavior of the painted bunting in southern Oklahoma. Bird-Banding, 30: 1–18.
1078. ———. 1964. Survival in the painted bunting. Living Bird, 3: 5–7.
1079. PARSONS, MRS. R. 1952. Observations on red-winged blackbirds. Iowa Bird Life, 22: 42.
1080. PATCH, C. L. 1918. A crow polygamist? Ottawa Nat., 32: 6.
1081. PATTEE, B. 1932. Nesting cardinals. Aud. Ann. Bull., 22: 56.
1082. PAUL, A. 1963. Some observations on tree swallows and finches in the western Chilcotin District of British Columbia. Murrelet, 44: 10–11.
1083. PAYNE, R. M. 1957. Nesting mockingbirds. Maine Field Nat., 13: 91.
1084. PAYNE, R. S. 1923. The Baltimore oriole and a biographical sketch of Audubon. Norman, Remington Co., Baltimore. 55 pp.
1085. PEABODY, P. B. 1899. The prairie horned lark. Osprey, 3: 118–119.
1086. ———. 1905. The Tolmie warbler in Wyoming. Warbler, 1(second series): 77–80.
1087. ———. 1907a. Rock wren the cliff dweller. Warbler, 3(second series): 7–14.
1088. ———. 1907b. The crossbills of northeastern Wyoming. Auk, 24: 271–278.
1089. ———. 1909. Chat the pantaloon. Warbler 5(second series): 10–14.
1090. ———. 1928. Nesting of the Cassin purple finch. Ool., 45: 164.
1091. PEABODY, W. B. O. 1840. A report on the birds of Massachusetts made to the legislature in the session of 1838–9. Boston Jour. Nat. Hist., 3: 65–266.
1092. PEARSON, T. G. 1905. A bluebird and his mate. Bird-Lore, 7: 210.
1093. ———. 1919. The red-eyed vireo. Bird-Lore, 21: 266–269.
1094. ———. 1921. Brown creeper. Bird-Lore, 23: 60–63.

1095. ———. 1922. Maryland yellow-throat. Bird-Lore, 24: 62–65.
1096. PEARSON, T. G., C. S. BRIMLEY, AND H. H. BRIMLEY. 1942. Birds of North Carolina. Bynum Printing Co., Raleigh, N. C. 416 pp.
1097. PEARSON, T. G., et al. 1936. Birds of America. Garden City Pub. Co., Inc., Garden City, N. Y. V. 2, 271 pp.; V. 3, 289 pp.
1098. PEASE, C. E. 1926. A cat with catbirds. Bull. Mass. Aud. Soc., 10(2): 4.
1099. PEPPER, W. 1912. A myrtle warbler nest. Bird-Lore, 14: 15–16.
1100. PERKINS, S. E., III. 1926. Peculiar behavior of a kingbird at an orchard oriole's nest. Wils. Bull., 38: 158–159.
1101. ———. 1938. Additional notes on birds of Lake Maxinkuckee Region. Am. Mid. Nat., 20: 540–548.
1102. PERRY, A. E. 1964. The nesting of the pine siskin in Nebraska. Wils. Bull., 77: 243–250.
1103. PERRY, E. M., AND W. A. PERRY. 1918. Home life of the vesper sparrow and the hermit thrush. Auk, 35: 310–321.
1104. PERRY, MRS. H. C. 1919. Bird neighbors. Bird-Lore, 21: 234–236.
1105. PETERSEN, A. J. 1955. The breeding cycle in the bank swallow. Wils. Bull., 67: 235–286.
1106. PETERSEN, A., AND H. YOUNG. 1950. A nesting study of the bronzed grackle. Auk, 67: 466–476.
1107. PETERSON, J. 1935. Western tanager nesting in Alum Rock Park, San José. Condor, 37: 286.
1108. PETERSON, R. T. 1936. The bluebird. Bird-Lore, 38: 129–132.
1109. ———. 1946. Nesting sites of the parula warbler in the Potomac Valley. Wils. Bull., 58: 197.
1110. PETRIDES, G. A. 1938. A life history study of the yellow-breasted chat. Wils. Bull., 50: 184–189.
1111. ———. 1942. Variable nesting habits of the parula warbler. Wils. Bull., 54: 252–253.
1112. PETTINGILL, E. R. 1937. Grand Manan's acadian chickadees. Bird-Lore, 39: 277–282.
1113. PETTINGILL, O. S., JR. 1930. Observations of the nesting activities of the hermit thrush. Bird-Banding, 1: 72–77.
1114. ———. 1942. The birds of a bull's horn acacia. Wils. Bull., 54: 89–96.
1115. ———. 1957. Horned larks nesting at Augusta airport. Maine Field Nat., 13: 58–59.
1116. ———. 1963. All-day observations at a robin's nest. Living Bird, 2: 47–55.
1117. PHILLIPS, A. R. 1949. Nesting of the rose-throated becard in Arizona. Condor, 51: 137–139.
1118. PHILLIPS, A., J. MARSHALL, AND G. MONSON. 1964. The birds of Arizona. Univ. of Arizona Press, Tucson. 220 pp.
1119. PHILLIPS, B. M. 1906. The inconstancy of mother wren. Amer. Ornith., 6: 40–41.
1120. PHILIPP, P. B. 1925. Notes on some summer birds of the Magdalen Islands. Can. Field Nat., 39: 75–78.
1121. PICKWELL, G. B. 1931. The prairie horned lark. Trans. St. Louis Acad. Sci., 27: 1–153.
1122. ———. 1947. The American pipit in its arctic–alpine home. Auk, 64: 1–14.
1123. PIELOU, W. P. 1957. A life history study of the tufted titmouse, Parus bicolor Linnaeus. Mich. State Univ. Dissert. Abstr. 20[1]: 1107–1108.
1124. PIERCE, F. J. 1931. The yellow-throated vireo nesting in Buchanan County, Iowa. Wils. Bull., 43: 312.
1125. PIERCE, W. M. 1907. Experiences with the dotted canyon wren. Condor, 9: 16–17.
1126. PIRNIE, M. D. 1943. Bird-house nuthatches. Jack-Pine Warb., 21: 71–72.
1127. PITELKA, F. A. 1940. Breeding behavior of the black-throated green warbler. Wils. Bull., 52: 3–18.
1128. PITELKA, F. A., AND E. J. KOESTNER. 1942. Breeding behavior of Bell's vireo in Illinois. Wils. Bull., 54: 97–106.
1129. PITTMAN, H. H. 1960. A "good samaritan." Aud. Mag., 62: 168–169.
1130. PLEAS, L. 1891. The blue-gray gnat-catcher in Arkansas. Ool., 8: 239–240.
1131. POPE, A. 1908. Nest-building in August. Bird-Lore, 10: 214–215.
1132. PORTER, B. C. 1905. The nest in the meadow. Amer. Ornith., 5: 187–190.
1133. POSSON, N. F. 1893. The rose-breasted grosbeak at home. Ool., 10: 253–254.

1134. Post, K. C. 1916. The cedar waxwing (*Bombycilla cedrorum*) during July and August, 1916. Wils. Bull., 28: 175–193.
1135. Power, H. W., III. 1966. Biology of the mountain bluebird in Montana. Condor, 68: 351–371.
1136. Prescott, C. S. 1906. Bobolink. Ool., 23: 165–166.
1137. Prescott, K. W. 1964. Constancy of incubation for the scarlet tanager. Wils. Bull., 76: 37–42.
1138. Preston, F. W. 1944. Nesting behavior of certain individual American robins. Aud. Mag., 46: 249–250.
1139. Preston, J. W. 1889. The blackburnian warbler at home. Ornith. and Ool., 14: 34–35.
1140. ———. 1909. Swarming of the ruby-crowned kinglet. Condor, 11: 93.
1141. Price, J. B. 1936. The family relations of the plain titmouse. Condor, 38: 23–28.
1142. Price, M. H. 1903. Mrs. Chickadee's trials. Amer. Ornith., 3: 302–303.
1143. Price, W. W. 1895. The nest and eggs of the olive warbler (*Dendroica olivacea*). Auk, 12: 17–19.
1144. Proc. of the ornithological sub-section of the biological section of the Canadian Institute, 1890 (Jan.–Mar.).
1145. Proescholdt, Mrs. C. 1958. Birds in our backyard. Iowa Bird Life, 28: 34–36.
1146. ———. 1959. Color selectivity in nesting material of a Baltimore oriole. Iowa Bird Life, 29: 104.
1147. Purdie, H. A. 1878. The black-throated bunting (*Euspiza americana*) nesting in Massachusetts. Bull. Nuttall Orn. Club, 3: 45.
1148. Purdy, J. B. 1889. Nesting habits of the white-bellied nuthatch, *Sitta carolinensis*. Ornith. and Ool. Semi-annual (Wils. Bull.), 1(2): 40–41.
1149. Putnam, L. S. 1949. The life history of the cedar waxwing. Wils. Bull., 61: 141–182.
1150. Quinn, J. L. 1955. An unsuccessful bluebird nest. Pass. Pigeon, 17: 154–155.
1151. Rand, A. L. 1946. List of Yukon birds and those of the Canol Road. Nat. Mus. of Can., Bull. 105, Biol. Series, 33: 1–76.
1152. Rand, A. L., and R. M. Rand. 1943. Breeding notes on the phainopepla. Auk, 60: 333–341.
1153. Randle, F. 1919. Pocket sanctuary. Bird-Lore, 21: 219–223.
1154. Randle, W. S. 1963. A solitary vireo found nesting in south-central Ohio's Hocking County. Wils. Bull., 75: 277–278.
1155. Rathbun, F. R. 1885. The cedar bird. Ornith. and Ool., 10: 174–175.
1156. Ray, M. S. 1910. The discovery of the nest and eggs of the gray-crowned leucosticte. Condor, 12: 147–161.
1157. ———. 1912. The discovery of the nest and eggs of the California pine grosbeak. Condor, 14: 157–187.
1158. Raynor, G. S. 1964. Nesting of the blue-gray gnatcatcher on Long Island, New York. Auk, 81: 552–553.
1159. Rea, G. 1945. Black and white warbler feeding young of worm-eating warbler. Wils. Bull., 57: 262.
1160. Reading, D. K., and S. P. Hayes, Jr. 1933. Notes on the nesting and feeding of a pair of black-throated green warblers. Auk, 50: 403–407.
1161. Redfield, A. C. 1911. A yellow-throat family. Bird-Lore, 13: 195–197.
1162. Reed, Mrs. A. C. 1946. Saga of a mockingbird. Raven, 17: 31–40.
1163. Reed, C. A. 1901a. Scarlet tanager. Amer. Ornith., 1: 128–131.
1164. ———. 1901b. California bush-tit. Amer. Ornith., 1: 87–89.
1165. ———. 1902a. Field sparrow. Amer. Ornith., 2: 229–233.
1167. ———. 1902b. American redstart. Amer. Ornith., 2: 303–308.
1168. ———. 1902c. Red-eyed vireo. Amer. Ornith., 2: 316–324.
1169. ———. 1903a. Prairie warbler. Amer. Ornith., 3: 63–69.
1170. ———. 1903b. Cedar bird. Amer. Ornith., 3: 122–131.
1171. ———. 1903c. Western chipping sparrow. Amer. Ornith., 3: 157–165.
1172. ———. 1904a. Black-throated green warbler. Amer. Ornith., 4: 40–43.
1173. ———. 1904b. Chestnut-sided warbler. Amer. Ornith., 4: 83–84.
1174. ———. 1905a. Salt marsh yellow-throat. Amer. Ornith., 5: 11–13.
1175. ———. 1905b. Tufted titmouse. Amer. Ornith., 5: 223–225.
1176. ———. 1905c. An interesting family. Amer. Ornith., 5: 272–274.

1177. REED, J. H. 1897. Breeding of the rose-breasted grosbeak at Beverly, New Jersey. Auk, 14: 323.
1178. REID, R. 1929. Nesting of the pine siskin in North Dakota. Wils. Bull., 41: 72–74.
1179. REIF, C. B. 1941. Courtship and nesting of the red-eyed vireo. Flicker, 13: 35–36.
1180. REINECKE, E. 1900. The brown creeper, *Certhia familiaris americana*, Ridgw. Ool., 17: 8–9.
1181. ———. 1908. The mourning warbler. Ool., 25: 22–23.
1182. RICHARDS, G. 1908. An unusual nesting locality for the Rocky Mountain nuthatch. Condor, 10: 194–195.
1183. RIDGWAY, R. 1889. The ornithology of Illinois, Vol. 1. Illinois Nat. Hist. Survey. H. W. Rokker, Springfield. 520 pp.
1184. RIEGEL, MRS. J. A. 1954. A nesting warbling vireo. Pass. Pigeon, 16: 111–112.
1185. ROADS, M. K. 1932a. Nest construction of the blue-gray gnatcatcher. Auk, 49: 90–91.
1186. ———. 1932b. The nesting behavior of a pair of mockingbirds. Wils. Bull., 44: 188–189.
1187. ———. 1932c. Blue jays gathering twigs for nests. Auk, 49: 223.
1188. ROBERTS, A. R. 1920. Cedar farm and two wrens. Bird-Lore, 22: 143–145.
1189. ROBERTS, T. S. 1899. The camera as an aid in the study of birds. Bird-Lore, 1: 6–13, 35–38.
1190. ———. 1909. A study of a breeding colony of yellow-headed blackbirds; including an account of the destruction of the entire progeny of the colony by some unknown natural agency. Auk, 26: 371–389.
1191. ———. 1914. Brewer's blackbird (*Euphagus cyanocephalus*) breeding in southeastern Minnesota. Auk, 31: 538–540.
1192. ———. 1922. The season: Minneapolis (Minnesota) region. Bird-Lore, 24: 283–284.
1193. ———. 1932. The birds of Minnesota. Part 2. Univ. of Minn. Press, Minneapolis. 821 pp.
1194. ROBINSON, H. J. 1927. Tree swallow habits and behavior at Brewer, Maine. Bull. N. E. Bird-Banding Assoc., 3: 89–93.
1195. ———. 1928. Domestic vicissitudes of bluebirds. Bull. N. E. Bird-Banding Assoc., 4: 21–25.
1196. ROLFE, E. S. 1897. Minor nesting notes from North Dakota. Nidol., 4: 88–91.
1197. ROSENWINKEL, A. C. 1956. Chickadees excavate nesting cavity. Flicker, 28: 39.
1198. ROSS, F. S. 1904. An oriole's nest. Amer. Ornith., 4: 57–58.
1199. RUDOLPHI, A. 1935. Study of nesting habits of a chipping sparrow. Mich. Biol. Sta., MS. *In* Kendeigh, 1952.
1200. RUSSELL, H. N., JR., AND A. M. WOODBURY. 1941. Nesting of the gray flycatcher. Auk, 58: 28–37.
1201. RUSSELL, W. C. 1947. Mountain chickadees feeding young Williamson sapsuckers. Condor, 49: 83.
1202. RUST, H. J. 1920. The home life of the western warbling vireo. Condor, 22: 85–94.
1203. SAGE, J. H. 1889. The interbreeding of *Helminthophila pinus* and *H. chrysoptera*. Auk, 6: 279.
1204. SALOMONSEN, F. 1950. The birds of Greenland. Ejnar Munksgaard, Copenhagen. 608 pp.
1205. SAMSON, P. C. 1923. The nest on the rain pipe. Bird-Lore, 25: 105–107.
1206. SAMUELS, E. A. 1870. The birds of New England. Noyes, Holmes, and Co., Boston. 591 pp.
1207. SARGENT, G. T. 1940. Observations on the behavior of color-banded California thrashers. Condor, 42: 49–60.
1208. SAUNDERS, A. A. 1910. Bird notes from southwestern Montana. Condor, 12: 195–204.
1209. ———. 1911. A study of the nesting of the cedar waxwing. Auk, 28: 323–329.
1210. ———. 1914. An ecological study of the breeding birds of an area near Choteau, Mont. Auk, 31: 200–210.
1211. ———. 1915. The fearless white-eyed vireo. Wils. Bull., 27: 316–321.
1212. ———. 1929. The summer birds of the northern Adirondack Mountains. Roosevelt Wild Life Bull., 5: 327–499.
1213. ———. 1938. Studies of breeding birds in the Allegheny State Park. New York State Mus. Bull., 318: 1–160.

1214. SAWYER, D. 1947. Nesting of chestnut-sided warbler. Auk, 63: 136–137.
1215. SCHANTZ, O. M. 1912. Prothonotary warblers (*Protonotaria citrea*) nesting at River-side, Illinois. Wils. Bull., 24: 165–167.
1216. SCHANTZ, W. E. 1937. A nest-building male song sparrow. Auk, 54: 189–191.
1217. ———. 1939. A detailed study of a family of robins. Wils. Bull., 51: 157–169.
1218. ———. 1944. All-day record of an incubating robin. Wils. Bull., 56: 118.
1219. SCHAUB, B. M. 1951. Young evening grosbeaks, *Hesperiphona vespertina*, at Saranac Lake, New York, 1949. Auk, 68: 517–519.
1220. SCHLAG, C. W. 1931. The struggle for existence. Cardinal, 3: 34–35.
1221. SCHRANTZ, F. G. 1943. Nest life of the eastern yellow warbler. Auk, 60: 367–387.
1222. SCOTT, A. L. 1906. Nature's early guests. Amer. Ornith., 6: 65–68.
1223. SCOTT, MRS. W. E. 1943. Orchard oriole nests in Dane County. Pass. Pigeon, 5: 48–49.
1224. SCOTT, W. E. D. 1885. On the breeding habits of some Arizona birds. Auk, 2: 321–326.
1225. SELANDER, R. K. 1961. Supplemental data on the sex ratio in nestling boat-tailed grackles. Condor, 63: 504.
1226. ———. 1965. On mating systems and sexual selection. Am. Nat., 99: 129–141.
1227. SELANDER, R. K., AND D. R. GILLER. 1961. Analysis of sympatry of great-tailed and boat-tailed grackles. Condor, 63: 29–86.
1228. SELANDER, R. K., AND R. J. HAUSER. 1965. Gonadal and behavioral cycles in the great-tailed grackle. Condor, 67: 157–182.
1229. SELBY, G. P. 1941. A contribution to the life history of the prairie horned lark on Long Island. Birds of Long Island, 4: 83–88.
1230. SEEMAN, E. 1906. A wren family. Amer. Ornith., 6: 134–136.
1231. SEMPLE, J. B., AND G. M. SUTTON. 1932. Nesting of Harris's sparrow (*Zonotrichia querula*) at Churchill, Manitoba. Auk, 49: 166–183.
1232. SENNETT, G. B. 1878. Notes on the ornithology of the Lower Rio Grande of Texas, from observations made during the season of 1877. Bull. U. S. Geol. and Geog. Survey, 4: 1–66.
1233. ———. 1879. Further notes on the ornithology of the Lower Rio Grande of Texas from observations made during the spring of 1878. Bull. U. S. Geol. and Geog. Survey, 5: 371–440.
1234. SHACKLETON, W. H. 1946. Nesting of the prothonotary warbler. Kentucky Warb., 22: 1–3.
1235. SHAVER, N. E. 1918. A nest study of the Maryland yellowthroat. Univ. of Iowa Studies in Nat. Hist., 8: 1–12.
1236. SHAW, H. S., JR. 1916. Some experiences in attracting birds—The nesting of a red-breasted nuthatch. Bird-Lore, 18: 166–170.
1237. SHAW, W. T. 1936. Winter life and nesting studies of Hepburn's rosy finch in Washington State. Auk, 53: 133–149.
1238. SHEAK, W. H. 1902. The catbird's nest. Ool., 19: 55.
1239. SHEPARDSON, D. I. 1915. Some western birds—phainopepla. Ool., 32: 144–145.
1240. SHERMAN, A. R. 1912. The brown thrasher, (*Toxostoma rufum*) east and west. Wils. Bull., 24: 187–191.
1241. ———. 1916. A peculiar habit of the house wren. Wils. Bull., 28: 94–95.
1242. ———. 1952. Birds of an Iowa dooryard. Christopher Publ. House, Boston. 270 pp.
1243. SHERMAN, J. W. 1910. The Brewster's warbler in Massachusetts. Auk, 27: 443–447.
1244. SHERRILL, W. E. 1896. Nidification of the white-necked raven. Nidol., 3: 110.
1245. SHIRLING, A. E. 1927. Tabulating the feeding of nestlings. Wils. Bull., 39: 13–15.
1246. SHORT, L. L., JR. 1964. Extra helpers feeding young of blue-winged and golden-winged warblers. Auk, 81: 428–430.
1247. SHORTT, T. M., AND S. WALLER. 1937. The birds of the Lake St. Martin region, Manitoba. Contr. Royal Ont. Mus. Zool., 10: 1–51.
1248. SHUFELDT, R. W. 1917. Interesting nests and eggs of some western birds. Ool., 34: 209–215.
1249. SIBLEY, C. G. 1955. Nesting of the western tanager in the Santa Cruz Mountains, California. Condor, 57: 307.
1250. SILLOWAY, P. M. 1900. Montana magpies. Ool., 17: 89–91.
1251. ———. 1901. Summer birds of Flathead Lake. Bull. Univ. of Montana, 3 (Biol. Series, 1): 1–83.

1252. ———. 1902. Notes of McCown's longspur in Montana. Osprey, 1 (New Series): 42–44.

1253. ———. 1903. The birds of Fergus County, Montana. Bull. Fergus Co. Free High School, 1: 1–77.

1254. ———. 1904. Afield at Flathead. Condor, 6: 12–14.

1255. ———. 1906. A novice's note-book, (No. 4). Ool., 23: 89–91.

1256. ———. 1919. Some nesting birds of the Palisades Interstate Park. Ool., 36: 13–16, 145–148, and 212–214.

1257. SIMMONS, G. F. 1915. On the nesting of certain birds in Texas. Auk, 32: 317–331.

1258. SIMPSON, R. B. 1910. The cerulean warbler. Ool., 27: 65–66.

1259. ———. 1912. The pine siskin. Ool., 29: 372–373.

1260. ———. 1914a. The winter wren. Ool., 31: 186–188.

1261. ———. 1914b. The solitary vireo. Ool., 31: 229–230.

1262. ———. 1920. Two May days. Ool., 37: 142–143.

1263. ———. 1921. The brown creeper. Ool., 38: 153–154.

1264. ———. 1922. Some blackburnian nests. Ool., 39: 86–87.

1265. SKINNER, M. P. 1916. The nutcrackers of Yellowstone Park. Condor, 18: 62–64.

1266. SKUTCH, A. F. 1935. Helpers at the nest. Auk, 52: 257–273.

1267. ———. 1954a. Life history of the tropical kingbird. Proc. Linn. Soc. of New York, 63–65: 21–38.

1268. ———. 1954b. Life histories of Central American birds. Pacific Coast Avif., 31: 1–448.

1269. ———. 1960. Life histories of Central American birds. II. Pacific Coast Avif., 34: 1–593.

1270. ———. 1961. Helpers among birds. Condor, 63: 198–226.

1271. ———. 1962. The constancy of incubation. Wils. Bull., 74: 115–152.

1272. SLOANMAKER, J. L. 1905. Adventures of a grosbeak family. Ool., 22: 24–25.

1273. SMART, M. F. 1905. Maine bird notes. Amer. Ornith., 5: 209–212.

1274. SMITH, P. W., JR. 1904. Nesting habits of the rock wren. Condor, 6: 109–110.

1275. SMITH, R. L. 1963. Some ecological notes on the grasshopper sparrow. Wils. Bull., 75: 159–165.

1276. SMITH, S. M. 1967. A case of polygamy in the black-capped chickadee. Auk, 84: 274.

1277. SMITH, W. 1947. Orchard orioles. Pass. Pigeon, 9: 8–16.

1278. SMITH, W. F. 1905. Blue jays at home. Bird-Lore, 7: 268–271.

1279. SMITH, W. P. 1925. Wells River (Vermont) bird notes. Bull. N. E. Bird-Banding Assoc., 1: 30–31.

1280. ———. 1928. The partial history of a pair of nesting juncos. Bull. N. E. Bird-Banding Assoc., 4: 137–141.

1281. ———. 1930. The further history of a nesting pair of juncos. Bird-Banding, 1: 36–40.

1282. ———. 1933. Some observations on the nesting habits of the barn swallow. Auk, 50: 414–419.

1283. ———. 1934. Observations of the nesting habits of the black-and-white warbler. Bird-Banding, 5: 31–35.

1284. ———. 1937a. Some bluebird observations. Bird-Banding, 8: 25–30.

1285. ———. 1937b. Further notes on the nesting of the barn swallow. Auk, 54: 65–69.

1286. ———. 1942. Nesting habits of the eastern phoebe. Auk, 59: 410–417.

1287. ———. 1943. Some yellow warbler observations. Bird-Banding, 14: 57–63.

1288. SMITHWICK, J. W. P. 1891. Nesting and other habits of the pine warbler in eastern North Carolina. Ornith. and Ool., 16: 119–120.

1289. SMITHWICK, R. P. 1899. The hooded and pine warblers in North Carolina. Ool., 16: 30–31.

1290. ———. 1905. In North Carolina and Virginia. *Polioptila caerulea*. Ool., 22: 117–119.

1291. SNYDER, D. E. 1950. New nesting records from Essex County. Bull. Mass. Aud. Soc., 34: 298–299.

1292. ———. 1952. Red crossbills. Bull. Mass. Aud. Soc., 36: 383–386.

1293. ———. 1954. A nesting study of red crossbills. Wils. Bull., 66: 32–37.

1294. ———. 1956. Shrikes nest in Essex County. Bull. Mass. Aud. Soc., 40: 431–435.

1295. SNYDER, L. L. 1919. Tragedies of the nest. Bird-Lore, 21: 230–233.

1296. SNYDER, L. L., AND E. B. S. LOGIER. 1930. A faunal investigation of King Township, York County, Ontario. Trans. Royal Can. Inst., 17: 167–208.

1297. SOPER, J. D. 1920. Nesting of the ruby-crowned kinglet at Guelph, Ontario. Can. Field Nat., 34: 72–73.

1298. SOUTHERN, W. E. 1958. Nesting of the red-eyed vireo in the Douglas Lake Region, Michigan. Jack-Pine Warb., 36: 105–130, 185–207.

1299. ———. 1959. Foster-feeding and polygamy in the purple martin. Wils. Bull., 71: 96.

1300. ———. 1962. Notes on the cerulean warbler life cycle. Pass. Pigeon, 24: 9–11.

1301. SPAULDING, P. 1924. Nesting notes from Conn. Ool., 41: 82–83.

1302. SPRAGUE, H. O. 1935. The oriole quintuplets. Bull. Mass. Aud. Soc., 19(3): 7–8.

1303. SPRINGER, P. 1942. Some observations on the breeding activities of the eastern king-bird (Tyrannus tyrannus). Mich. Biol. Sta., MS. In Kendeigh, 1952.

1304. SPRUNT, A., JR. 1951. Golden-cheek of the cedar brakes. Aud. Mag., 53: 13–16.

1305. SQUIRES, S. K. 1929. Barn swallows. Can. Field Nat., 43: 59–61.

1306. STAFFORD, E. F. 1912. Notes on Palmer's thrasher (Toxostoma curvirostre palmeri). Auk, 29: 363–368.

1307. STANFORD, J. A. 1942. Preliminary observations on the nesting activities of the eastern wood pewee (Myiochanes virens). Mich. Biol. Sta., MS. In Kendeigh, 1952.

1308. STANWOOD, C. J. 1909. Clever builders. Nest and young of the bay-breasted warbler. Jour. Maine Ornith. Soc., 11: 103–110.

1309. ———. 1910a. A lowly home, nest and young of the Nashville warbler. Jour. Maine Ornith. Soc., 12: 28–33.

1310. ———. 1910b. The black and white warbler. Jour. Maine Ornith. Soc., 12: 61–66.

1311. ———. 1910c. The black-throated green warbler. Auk, 27: 289–294.

1312. ———. 1910d. A series of nests of the magnolia warbler. Auk, 27: 384–389.

1313. ———. 1911. A study of two chickadee families. Jour. Maine Ornith. Soc., 13: 25–32.

1314. ———. 1913. The olive-backed thrush (Hylocichla ustulata swainsoni) at his summer home. Wils. Bull., 25: 118–137.

1315. ———. 1914. A brief study of the nest life of the black-throated green warbler. Wils. Bull., 26: 186–188.

1316. STEELE, MRS. R. G. 1916. Cardinals through the year. Bird-Lore, 18: 289–292.

1317. STEFANSKI, R. A. 1967. Utilization of the breeding territory in the black-capped chickadee. Condor, 69: 259–267.

1318. STEFFEN, E. W. 1945. Birds at my studio window. Iowa Bird Life, 15: 22–25.

1319. STEIGER, J. A. 1940. Dipper, wilderness dweller. Bird-Lore, 42: 10–14.

1320. STENGER, J., AND J. B. FALLS. 1959. The utilized territory of the ovenbird. Wils. Bull., 71: 125–139.

1321. STEPHENS, T. C. 1917. A study of a red-eyed vireo's nest which contained a cow-bird's egg. Univ. of Iowa Monographs. Bull. from the Lab. of Nat. Hist., 7: 25–38.

1322. STEVENS, C. E. 1960. The blue-winged warbler nesting in Rockingham County and summer notes on the golden-winged warbler in Rockingham and Albemarle Counties, Virginia. Raven, 31: 84–85.

1323. STEVENS, O. A. 1952. An unsuccessful early robin nest. Flicker, 24: 159.

1324. STEVENSON, H. M., JR. 1938. Bachman's warbler in Alabama. Wils. Bull., 50: 36–41.

1325. STEWART, R. E. 1953. A life history of the yellow-throat. Wils. Bull., 65: 99–115.

1326. STOKES, A. W. 1950. Breeding behavior of the goldfinch. Wils. Bull., 62: 107–127.

1327. STONE, C. F. 1901. Gleanings from my note book. Ool., 18: 71–73.

1328. STONE, W. 1937. Bird studies at old Cape May. Vol. 2. Delaware Valley Ornith. Club, Philadelphia. pp. 521–941.

1329. STONER, D. 1920. Nesting habits of the hermit thrush in northern Michigan. Univ. of Iowa Studies in Nat. Hist., 9: 1–21.

1330. ———. 1925. Observations and banding notes on the bank swallow. Auk, 42: 86–94.

1331. ———. 1932. Ornithology of the Oneida Lake Region: With reference to the late spring and summer seasons. Roosevelt Wild Life Ann., 2: 277–764.

1332. ———. 1936. Studies on the bank swallow, Riparia riparia riparia (Linnaeus), in the Oneida Lake Region. Roosevelt Wild Life Ann., 9: 126–233.

1333. STONER, D., AND L. C. STONER. 1941. Feeding of nestling bank swallows. Auk, 58: 52–55.

1334. STONER, E. A. 1934. Sleeping posture of house finches on the nest at night. Auk, 51: 92.

1335. STOPHLET, J. J. 1958. Hooded oriole nesting under eaves of house. Auk, 75: 221–222.

1336. STRAW, MRS. H. F. 1919. Purple finches. Bird-Lore, 21: 165–166.

1337. STRECKER, J. K., JR. 1893. Nesting of the painted bunting. Nidol., 1: 39–40.

1338. STROSNIDER, R. 1960. Polygyny and other notes on the redwinged blackbird. Wils. Bull., 72: 200.

1339. STUART, G. H., III. 1915. Days with the blue-gray gnatcatcher and the prothonotary warbler. Cassinia, 19: 24–29.

1340. STUPKA, A. 1963. Notes on the birds of the Great Smoky Mountains National Park. Univ. of Tenn. Press, Knoxville. 242 pp.

1341. STURM, L. 1945. A study of the nesting activities of the American redstart. Auk, 62: 189–206.

1342. STURMER, M. 1959. Nesting of the scissor-tailed flycatcher in Gage County. Nebraska Bird Review, 27: 19–20.

1343. SUTTER, J. H. 1920. The brown thrasher. Aud. Bull., 8: 16–17.

1344. SUTTON, G. M. 1920. Annotated list of the birds of Brooke County, W. Va. Part 3. Ool., 37: 76–80.

1345. ———. 1927. Flocking, mating, and nest-building habits of the prairie horned lark. Wils. Bull., 39: 131–141.

1346. ———. 1930. The nesting wrens of Brooke County, West Virginia. Wils. Bull., 42: 10–17.

1347. ———. 1932. The birds of Southampton Island. Mem. Carnegie Mus., 12: 1–275.

1348. ———. 1941. Crousty, the story of a redbird. Aud. Mag., 43: 161–168, 270–278.

1349. ———. 1948. The nest and eggs of the white-bellied wren. Condor, 50: 101–112.

1350. ———. 1949. Studies of the nesting birds of the Edwin S. George Reserve. Part 1. The vireos. Misc. Pub. Univ. of Mich. Mus. of Zool., 74: 1–37.

1351. ———. 1959. The nesting fringillids of the Edwin S. George Reserve, southeastern Michigan (Part 1). Jack-Pine Warb., 37: 3–11.

1352. SUTTON, G. M., AND D. F. PARMELEE. 1954a. Survival problems of the water pipit in Baffin Island. Arctic, 7: 81–92.

1353. ———. 1954b. Nesting of the snow bunting on Baffin Island. Wils. Bull., 66: 159–179.

1354. ———. 1954c. Nesting of the Greenland wheatear on Baffin Island. Condor, 56: 295–306.

1355. ———. 1955a. Nesting of the horned lark on Baffin Island. Bird-Banding, 26: 1–18.

1356. ———. 1955b. Summer activities of the Lapland longspur on Baffin Island. Wils. Bull., 67: 110–127.

1357. SUTTON, G. M., R. B. LEA, AND E. P. EDWARDS. 1950. Notes on the ranges and breeding habits of certain Mexican birds. Bird-Banding, 21: 45–59.

1358. SWALES, B. H. 1892. Rose-breasted grosbeak in Wayne Co., Mich. Ornith. and Ool., 17: 75.

1359. SWANSON, MRS. K. S. 1956. Aurora. Nebraska Bird Review, 24: 48–50.

1360. SWARTH, H. S. 1934. Birds of Nunivak Island, Alaska. Pacific Coast Avif., 22: 1–64.

1361. SWEDENBORG, E. D. 1929. Nest of golden-crowned kinglet in Millelacs County, Minnesota. Auk, 46: 121.

1362. SWEDENBORG, MRS. E. D. 1965. Notes on nesting evening grosbeaks at Loon Lake, Cass County. Loon, 37 (formerly Flicker): 151–152.

1363. SWEET, F. H. 1906. A bird of changed habits. Amer. Ornith., 6: 63–65.

1364. SWENK, M. H. 1921. Nesting of the red crossbill in Nebraska. Wils. Bull., 33: 38–39.

1365. ———. 1929. The pine siskin in Nebraska: its seasonal abundance and nesting. Wils. Bull., 41: 77–92.

1366. ———. 1936. A study of the distribution, migration and hybridism of the rose-breasted and Rocky Mountain black-headed grosbeaks in the Missouri Valley region. Nebraska Bird Review, 4: 27–40.

1367. T., H. 1888. Reminiscences of 1886. Ool., 5: 119–120.

1368. TABOR, E. G. 1890. Nesting of the mourning warbler. Ornith. and Ool., 15: 68–69.

1369. TANNER, J. T. 1958. Juncos in the Great Smoky Mountains. Migrant, 29: 61–65.

1370. TAPER, T. A. 1919. Two thrushes. Bird-Lore, 21: 167–169.
1371. TAYLOR, MRS. C. 1933. The purple martin. 1933 Indiana Aud. Soc. Yearbook: 101–105.
1372. TAYLOR, W. P. 1912. Field notes on amphibians, reptiles and birds of northern Humboldt County, Nevada. Univ. Calif. Pub. Zool., 7: 319–436.
1373. TAYLOR, W. A. 1947. Early bluebird breeding-record at Moose Hill. Bull. Mass. Aud. Soc., 31: 211.
1374. TEMPLETON, W. G. 1942. Spying on sister pewee. Chat, 6: 54–55, 75.
1375. TEN EYCK, E. F. 1907. A study of a house wren. Bird-Lore, 9: 201–203.
1376. TERRILL, L. McI. 1917. Horned larks in the province of Quebec. Wils. Bull., 29: 130–141.
1377. THAYER, H. C. 1901. Our blue jay neighbors. Bird-Lore, 3: 50–53.
1378. THAYER, M. R. 1912. Some nesting habits of the Oregon junco. Bird-Lore, 14: 212–215.
1379. THEODORE, BROTHER I., F. S. C. 1952. Bell's vireo in Winona County. Flicker, 24: 141–144.
1380. THOMAS, R. H. 1946a. A study of eastern bluebirds in Arkansas. Wils. Bull., 58: 143–183.
1381. ———. 1946b. An orchard oriole colony in Arkansas. Bird-Banding, 17: 161–167.
1382. THOMAS, R. R. 1950a. Crip, come home! Aud. Mag., 52: 172–177.
1383. ———. 1950b. Crip's last brood. Aud. Mag., 52: 288–293.
1384. ———. 1953. The constant Carolinas. Aud. Mag., 55: 9–11.
1385. ———. 1958. The bluebird that couldn't remember. Aud. Mag., 60: 114–115, 137.
1386. ———. 1961. Wren forever. Aud. Mag., 63: 16–17, 54–56.
1387. THOMPSON, E. E. 1891. The birds of Manitoba. Proc. U. S. Nat. Mus., 13: 457–643.
1388. THOMSON, H. W. 1914. The building of a robin's nest. Bird-Lore, 16: 360–361.
1389. THOMPSON, W. L. 1960. Agonistic behavior in the house finch. Pt. 1. Annual cycle and display patterns. Condor, 62: 245–271.
1390. THOMS, C. S. 1910. A chickadee home. Bird-Lore, 12: 220–225.
1391. ———. 1927. Winning the chickadee. Bird-Lore, 29: 191–192.
1392. THRONE, A. L. 1941. A nesting study of the eastern hermit thrush. Pass. Pigeon, 3: 13–16.
1393. ———. 1945. A nesting study of the eastern song sparrow. Pass. Pigeon, 7: 99–105.
1394. THURSTON, H. 1911. Long Island notes. Auk, 28: 276.
1395. TINBERGEN, N. 1939. The behavior of the snow bunting in spring. Trans. Linn. Soc. of New York, 5: 1–95.
1396. TINKHAM, E. R. 1949. Notes on nest-building of the vermilion flycatcher. Condor, 51: 230–231.
1397. TIPPENS, J. R. 1943. Bewick's wren nesting. Migrant, 14: 59.
1398. TODD, W. E. C. 1892. Nesting of the blue-gray gnatcatcher. Ornith. and Ool., 17: 73–74.
1399. ———. 1940. Birds of western Pennsylvania. Univ. of Pittsburgh Press, Pittsburgh. 710 pp.
1400. TOMKINS, I. R. 1941. Notes on Macgillivray's seaside sparrow. Auk, 58: 38–51.
1401. TOWER, K. D. 1919. Mr. and Mrs. Fearless. Bull. Mass. Aud. Soc., 3(2): 4–5.
1402. ———. 1922. Anisquam birds. Bull. Mass. Aud. Soc., 6(5): 6–7.
1403. TRACY, C. O. 1885. Rose-breasted grosbeak. (Zamelodia ludoviciana). Ornith. and Ool., 10: 37.
1404. TRAFTON, G. H. 1908. The nest in the gutter. Bird-Lore, 10: 72–76.
1405. TRAINOR, MRS. A. J. 1941. Purple finch nesting near St. Cloud. Flicker, 13: 34.
1406. TRAMONTANO, J. P. 1964. Comparative studies of the rock wren and the canyon wren. MS thesis, Univ. of Arizona Library, Tucson. 59 pp.
1407. TRAUTMAN, M. B. 1940. The birds of Buckeye Lake, Ohio. Misc. Pub. Mus. of Zool., Univ. of Mich., 44: 1–466.
1408. TREAT, M. 1881. The great crested flycatcher. Am. Nat., 15: 601–604.
1409. TREMBLY, C. C. 1892. A ramble in May. Ool., 9: 228–229.
1410. TRINE, MRS. G. W. 1935. Some Nebraska experiences with the northern purple martin. Nebraska Bird Review, 3: 79–82.
1411. ———. 1940. The northern purple martin as a neighbor. Nebraska Bird Review, 8: 45–49.
1412. TROTTER, W. H. 1931. A brood of ruby-crowns. Bird-Lore, 33: 190–191.
1413. TRUCHOT, E. K. 1964. Blue-gray gnatcatcher (Polioptila coerulea). Florida Nat., 37: 122.

1414. Tufts, H. F. 1906. Nesting of crossbills in Nova Scotia. Auk, 23: 339–340.
1415. Tufts, R. W. 1927. Banding of yellow warblers in Nova Scotia. Bull. N. E. Bird-Banding Assoc., 3: 3–5.
1416. ———. 1941. Late nesting of red-eyed vireo (*Vireo olivaceus*). Can. Field Nat., 55: 78.
1417. Turle, K. G. 1930. A nest of catbirds. Bird-Lore, 32: 133–134.
1418. Tutor, B. M. 1962. Nesting studies of the boat-tailed grackle. Auk, 79: 77–84.
1419. Tuttle, H. E. 1919. The warbler in stripes. Bird-Lore, 21: 296–298.
1420. Twining, H. 1938. The significance of combat in male rosy finches. Condor, 40: 246–247.
1421. Tyler, J. G. 1913. Some birds of the Fresno district, California. Pacific Coast Avif., 9: 1–114.
1422. Tyler, W. M. 1913. A successful pair of robins. Auk, 30: 394–398.
1423. ———. 1914. Notes on the nest life of the brown creeper in Massachusetts. Auk, 31: 50–62.
1424. Tyrrell, W. B. 1945. A study of the northern raven. Auk, 62: 1–7.
1425. Underwood, E. F. 1945. The vagaries of Jenny Wren. Bull. Mass. Aud. Soc., 29: 188.
1426. Van Fleet, C. C. 1919. A short paper on the Hutton vireo. Condor, 21: 162–165.
1427. Van Gilluwe, E. 1911. Nesting of the Carolina wren. Bird-Lore, 13: 149–150.
1428. Van Tyne, J. 1936. The discovery of the nest of the Colima warbler (*Vermivora crissalis*). Misc. Pub. Mus. Zool., Univ. of Mich., 33: 1–11.
1429. ———. 1951. A cardinal's, *Richmondena cardinalis,* choice of food for adult and for young. Auk, 68: 110.
1430. Van Tyne, J., and G. M. Sutton. 1937. The birds of Brewster County, Texas. Misc. Pub. Mus. of Zool., Univ. of Mich., 37: 1–119.
1431. Verbeek, N. A. M. 1967. Breeding biology and ecology of the horned lark in alpine tundra. Wils. Bull., 79: 208–218.
1432. Verner, J. 1963. Song rates and polygamy in the long-billed marsh wren. Proc. XIII Intern. Ornith. Congress: 299–307.
1433. ———. 1964. Evolution of polygamy in the long-billed marsh wren. Evol., 18: 252–261.
1434. ———. 1965a. Breeding biology of the long-billed marsh wren. Condor, 67: 6–30.
1435. ———. 1965b. Time budget of the male long-billed marsh wren during the breeding season. Condor, 67: 125–139.
1436. Verner, J., and M. F. Willson. 1966. The influence of habitats on mating systems of North American passerine birds. Ecol., 47: 143–147.
1437. Vickers, E. W. 1895. Notes on nidification of the white-breasted nuthatch. Ool., 12: 92–93.
1438. Vietor, K. P., and E. W. Vietor. 1912. Notes on cliff swallows. Bird-Lore, 14: 150–152.
1439. Von Steen, D. A. 1965. A study of nesting dickcissels in Nebraska. Nebraska Bird Review, 33: 22–24.
1440. Walkinshaw, L. H. 1931. The prothonotary warblers of the willow stub. Bird-Lore, 33: 176–178.
1441. ———. 1932. With Kirtland's warbler among the jack pines. Bird-Lore, 34: 196–199.
1442. ———. 1933. Myrtle warbler home-life. Bird-Lore, 35: 195–198.
1443. ———. 1935. Studies of the short-billed marsh wren (*Cistothorus stellaris*) in Michigan. Auk, 52: 362–369.
1444. ———. 1936. Notes on the field sparrow in Michigan. Wils. Bull., 48: 94–101.
1445. ———. 1937a. A study of the American goldfinch. Jack-Pine Warb., 15(3): 10.
1446. ———. 1937b. Leconte's sparrow breeding in Michigan and South Dakota. Auk, 54: 309–320.
1447. ———. 1938a. Life history studies of the eastern goldfinch. Jack-Pine Warb., 16(4): 3–11.
1448. ———. 1938b. Nesting studies of the prothonotary warbler. Bird-Banding, 9: 32–46.
1449. ———. 1939a. Life history studies of the eastern goldfinch. Part 2. Jack-Pine Warb., 17: 3–12.
1450. ———. 1939b. Notes on the nesting of the clay-colored sparrow. Wils. Bull., 51: 17–21.

1451. ———. 1939c. Additional information on the prothonotary warbler. Jack-Pine Warb., 17: 64–71.

1452. ———. 1939d. Nesting of the field sparrow and survival of the young. Bird-Banding, 10: 107–114, 149–157.

1453. ———. 1940. Some Michigan notes on the grasshopper sparrow. Jack-Pine Warb., 18: 50–59.

1454. ———. 1941. The prothonotary warbler, a comparison of nesting conditions in Tennessee and Michigan. Wils. Bull., 53: 3–21.

1455. ———. 1944a. Clay-colored sparrow notes. Jack-Pine Warb., 22: 120–131.

1456. ———. 1944b. The eastern chipping sparrow in Michigan. Wils. Bull., 56: 193–205.

1457. ———. 1945. Field sparrow, 39-54015. Bird-Banding, 16: 1–14.

1458. ———. 1948a. Nestings of some passerine birds in western Alaska. Condor, 50: 64–70.

1459. ———. 1948b. Brown creeper nesting in Calhoun County, Michigan. Jack-Pine Warb., 26: 157–158.

1460. ———. 1952. Observations on the pine warbler in Michigan. Jack-Pine Warb., 30: 94–99.

1461. ———. 1953. Life-history of the prothonotary warbler. Wils. Bull., 65: 152–168.

1462. ———. 1959a. The prairie warbler in Michigan. Jack-Pine Warb., 37: 54–63.

1463. ———. 1959b. A chipping sparrow nest in which eight eggs were laid and seven young reared. Auk, 76: 101–102.

1464. ———. 1966. Studies of the Acadian flycatcher in Michigan. Bird-Banding, 37: 227–257.

1465. WALKINSHAW, L. H., AND W. A. DYER. 1953. Nesting of the black-throated blue warbler in Michigan. Jack-Pine Warb., 31: 47–54.

1466. ———. 1954. Brown-capped chickadee nesting in Michigan. Jack-Pine Warb., 32: 107–109.

1467. ———. 1961. The Connecticut warbler in Michigan. Auk, 78: 379–388.

1468. WALKINSHAW, L. H., et al. 1957. Yellow-headed blackbird nesting in Michigan. Wils. Bull., 69: 183.

1469. WALKINSHAW, L. H., AND C. J. HENRY. 1957. Yellow-bellied flycatcher nesting in Michigan. Auk, 74: 293–304.

1470. WALKINSHAW, L. H., AND M. A. WOLF. 1957. Distribution of the palm warbler and its status in Michigan. Wils. Bull., 69: 338–351.

1471. WALKINSHAW, L. H., AND D. A. ZIMMERMAN. 1961. Range expansion of the Brewer blackbird in eastern North America. Condor, 63: 162–177.

1472. WALLACE, G. J. 1939. Bicknell's thrush, its taxonomy, distribution, and life history. Proc. Bost. Soc. Nat. Hist., 41: 211–402.

1473. WARBURTON, F. E. 1952. Nesting of clay-colored sparrow, *Spizella pallida*, in northern Ontario. Auk, 69: 314–316.

1474. WARING, MRS. M. M. 1912. Bluebirds vs. Wrens. Bird-Lore, 14: 293–294.

1475. WARREN, B. H. 1890. Report on the birds of Pennsylvania. E. K. Meyers, Harrisburg. 434 pp.

1476. WARREN, O. B. 1899. A chapter in the life of the Canada jay. Auk, 16: 12–19.

1477. WASHBURN, V. E. 1957. Hunt for an ouzel's nest. Aud. Mag., 59: 162–164.

1478. WATSON, G. E. 1963. A simultaneous nesting of the robin and the blue jay in one tree. Auk, 80: 377–378.

1479. WATTS, G. E. 1952. Life history of the rose-breasted grosbeak, *Hedymeles ludoviciana*. Ph.D. Dissertation, Cornell Univ. Library, Ithaca, New York.

1480. WAYNE, A. T. 1888a. Nesting of the brown-headed nuthatch in South Carolina. Ornith. and Ool., 13: 21–23.

1481. ———. 1888b. Nesting of the yellow-throated warbler near Charleston, S. C. Ornith. and Ool., 13: 161–162.

1482. ———. 1897. A remarkable nest of the tufted titmouse. Auk, 14: 98–99.

1483. ———. 1905. Notes on certain birds taken or seen near Charleston, South Carolina. Auk, 22: 395–400.

1484. ———. 1907. The nest and eggs of Bachman's warbler, *Helminthophila bachmani* (Aud.), taken near Charleston, South Carolina. Auk, 24: 43–48.

1485. ———. 1910. Birds of South Carolina. Contr. #1 from Charleston Museum. 254 pp.

1486. ———. 1919. The nest and eggs of Wayne's warbler (*Dendroica virens waynei*) taken near Mount Pleasant, S. C. Auk, 36: 489–492.

1487. WEAVER, F. G. 1939. Studies in the life history of the wood thrush. Bird-Banding, 10: 16–23.
1488. WEAVER, R. L., AND F. H. WEST. 1943. Notes on the breeding of the pine siskin. Auk, 60: 492–504.
1489. WEBB, R. J. 1903. Nest-building habits of the chickadee. Bird-Lore, 5: 63–64.
1490. WEBER, A. J. 1954. Weaklings among young purple martins. Iowa Bird Life, 24: 57.
1491. WEBSTER, MRS. C. P. 1898. Incidents in the lives of purple finches. Osprey, 3: 19.
1492. WEEDEN, J. S. 1966. Diurnal rhythm of attentiveness of incubating female tree sparrows (Spizella arborea) at a northern latitude. Auk, 83: 368–388.
1493. WEEKS, L. T. 1923. Who builds the nest? Bird-Lore, 25: 254–255.
1494. WELBORN, H. G. 1895. Blue-gray gnatcatcher. Ool., 12: 139–141.
1495. WELLMAN, G. B. 1905. A black and white creeper family. Bird-Lore, 7: 170–172.
1496. WELLS, MRS. R. H. 1946. Nest of the winter wren. Flicker, 18: 23–25.
1497. WELTER, W. A. 1935. The natural history of the long-billed marsh wren. Wils. Bull., 47: 3–34.
1498. WERNER, R. C. 1945. Kentucky warbler (Oporornis formosus) nest in Atlanta. Oriole, 10: 31.
1499. WESTON, F. M. 1947. Barn swallow nesting in Florida. Auk, 64: 472–473.
1500. ———. 1952. Hybrid (?) thrasher near Pensacola. Florida Nat., 25: 39.
1501. WESTON, H. G., JR. 1947. Breeding behavior of the black-headed grosbeak. Condor, 49: 54–73.
1502. WETHERBEE, MRS. K. B. 1933a. Some complicated bluebird family history. Bird-Banding, 4: 114–115.
1503. ———. 1933b. Three tree swallows feed a family of nestlings. Bird-Banding, 4: 116.
1504. WETMORE, A. 1918. Birds observed near Minco, central Oklahoma. Wils. Bull., 30: 2–10, 56–61.
1505. ———. 1920. Observations on the habits of birds at Lake Burford, New Mexico. Auk, 37: 221–247, 393–412.
1506. WEYDEMEYER, W. 1933. An unusual Montana junco nest. Bird-Lore, 35: 155–156.
1507. ———. 1934. Tree swallows at home in Montana. Bird-Lore, 36: 100–105.
1508. WEYGANDT, C. 1910. The wood thrush. Cassinia, 14: 21–27.
1509. WHARRAM, S. V. 1914. Nest notes. Ool., 31: 6–7.
1510. WHEDON, A. D. 1938. Nesting behavior of kingbirds. Wils. Bull., 50: 288–289.
1511. WHEELER, R. 1940. Nesting habits of the leucosticte. Condor, 42: 133–139.
1512. WHEELOCK, I. G. 1904. Birds of California. A. C. McClurg and Co., Chicago. 578 pp.
1513. ———. 1905. Regurgitative feeding of nestlings. Auk, 22: 54–71.
1514. WHITE, K. B. 1944. A nesting study of the red-eyed vireo, Vireo olivaceous (Linnaeus). Mich. Biol. Sta., MS. In Kendeigh, 1952.
1515. WHITFIELD, I. H. 1920. Yellow-throated vireos. Bird-Lore, 22: 288–289.
1516. WHITMAN, F. N. 1920. Field sparrows. Bird-Lore, 22: 81–83.
1517. WHITTEN, E. M. 1902. A home in a cellar. Bird-Lore, 4: 95–96.
1518. WHITTLE, C. L. 1938. An estimate of the sex ratio of the rose-breasted grosbeak (Hedymeles ludovicianus) with comments on the species. Bird-Banding, 9: 196–197.
1519. WHITTLE, H. G. 1923. Recent experiences with nesting catbirds. Auk, 40: 603–606.
1520. ———. 1925. Catbird history. Bull. N. E. Bird-Banding Assoc., 1: 48–49.
1521. ———. 1926. Recent history of a pair of white-breasted nuthatches, Nos. 117455 male and 117456 female. Bull. N. E. Bird-Banding Assoc., 2: 72–74.
1522. WIDMANN, O. 1884. How young birds are fed. Forest and Stream, 22: 484.
1523. ———. 1902. List of birds observed in the neighborhood of Wequetonsing, Emmet Co., Mich., July 9 to July 23, 1901. Auk, 19: 232–237.
1524. ———. 1922. Extracts from the diary of Otto Widmann. Trans. St. Louis Acad. Sci., 24: 1–77.
1525. WIENS, J. A. 1965. Behavioral interactions of red-winged blackbirds and common grackles on a common breeding ground. Auk, 82: 356–374.
1526. WIGHT, E. M. 1934. Attracting birds at Chattanooga. Migrant, 5: 46.
1527. WILDE, M. L. C. 1897. Nesting of the parula warbler (Compsothlypis americana) in Cape May County, New Jersey. Auk, 14: 289–294.
1528. WILLARD, F. C. 1908. Three vireos: Nesting notes from the Huachuca Mountains. Condor, 10: 230–234.

1529. ———. 1910a. Nesting of the western evening grosbeak (*Hesperiphona vespertina montana*). Condor, 12: 60–62.
1530. ———. 1910b. The olive warbler (*Dendroica olivacea*) in southern Arizona. Condor, 12: 104–107.
1531. ———. 1912a. A week afield in southern Arizona. Condor, 14: 53–63.
1532. ———. 1912b. Breeding of the Scott sparrow. Condor, 14: 195–196.
1533. ———. 1912c. Nesting of the Rocky Mountain nuthatch. Condor, 14: 213–215.
1534. ———. 1913. The verdin. Ool., 30: 78–79.
1535. ———. 1923a. The Mexican cliff swallow in Cochise County, Arizona. Condor, 25: 138–139.
1536. ———. 1923b. The buff-breasted flycatcher in the Huachucas. Condor, 25: 189–194.
1537. WILLETT, G. 1917. Further notes on the birds of Forrester Island. Condor, 19: 15–17.
1538. WILLIAMS, J. 1919. Purple martins at St. Marks, Florida. Wils. Bull., 31: 71–83.
1539. WILLIAMS, L. 1942. Interrelations in a nesting group of four species of birds. Wils. Bull., 54: 238–249.
1540. ———. 1952. Breeding behavior of the Brewer blackbird. Condor, 54: 3–47.
1541. WILLIAMS, L., K. LEGG, AND F. S. L. WILLIAMSON. 1958. Breeding of the parula warbler at Point Lobos, California. Condor, 60: 345–354.
1542. WILLSON, M. F. 1966a. Breeding ecology of the yellow-headed blackbird. Ecol. Monog., 36: 51–77.
1543. ———. 1966b. Polygamy among swamp sparrows. Auk, 83: 666.
1544. WILLSON, M. F., AND G. H. ORIANS. 1963. Comparative ecology of red-winged and yellow-headed blackbirds during the breeding season. Proc. XVI Intern. Zool. Congress, 3: 342–346.
1545. WILSON, B. H. 1906. The birds of Scott County, Iowa. Wils. Bull., 18: 1–11.
1546. ———. 1912. Red-letter days in the country. Ool., 29: 281–285.
1547. WILSON, F. N. 1929. Among the bulrushes. Bird-Lore, 31: 243–248.
1548. ———. 1930. The dickcissel's secret. Bird-Lore, 32: 331–334.
1549. ———. 1931. An uncommon Michigan sparrow. Bird-Lore, 33: 108–110.
1550. WILSON, G. 1923. Migrant shrike nesting in Kentucky. Wils. Bull., 35: 119.
1551. WING, L. W. 1933. Summer warblers of Crawford County, Michigan, uplands. Wils. Bull., 45: 70–76.
1552. WITSCHY, MRS. R. 1958. Yellow warblers at the nest. Nebraska Bird Review, 26: 18–19.
1553. WOOD, H. B. 1937a. The growth of young barn swallows. Bird-Banding, 8: 31–34.
1554. ———. 1937b. Observations at a barn swallow's nest. Wils. Bull., 49: 96–100.
1555. WOOD, J. C. 1906. The cerulean warbler. Ool., 23: 42–44.
1556. WOOD, N. A. 1904a. Discovery of the breeding area of Kirtland's warbler. Bull. Mich. Ornith. Club, 5: 3–13.
1557. ———. 1904b. The discovery of the first known nest of Kirtland's warbler. Ool., 21: 53–55.
1558. ———. 1926. In search of new colonies of Kirtland warblers. Wils. Bull., 38: 11–13.
1559. WOOD, O. C. 1922. The A. M. S. Robins. Bird-Lore, 24: 266–268.
1560. WOODBURY, A. M. 1939. Observations on the breeding of the western chipping sparrow. Ool., 56: 114–116.
1561. WOODBURY, A. M., AND H. N. RUSSELL, JR. 1945. Birds of the Navajo country. Bull. Univ. of Utah, 35: 4–157.
1562. WOODS, R. S. 1921. Home life of the black-tailed gnatcatcher. Condor, 23: 173–178.
1563. ———. 1924. Some birds of the San Gabriel Wash. Bird-Lore, 26: 1–9.
1564. ———. 1928. Nesting of the black-tailed gnatcatcher. Condor, 30: 139–143.
1565. WOOLFENDEN, G. E. 1956. Comparative breeding behavior of *Ammospiza caudacuta* and *A. maritima*. Pub. Univ. of Kansas Mus. Nat. Hist., 10: 45–75.
1566. WOOLLEN, W. W. 1907. Birds of Buzzard's Roost. One for each week. Scott-Miller, Indianapolis. 335 pp.
1567. WRIGHT, A. H., AND F. HARPER. 1913. A biological reconnaissance of Okefinokee Swamp: The birds. Auk, 30: 477–505.
1568. WRIGHT, H. W. 1909. A nesting of the blue-winged warbler in Massachusetts. Auk, 26: 337–345.

1569. Wright, M. O. 1907a. The red-winged blackbird. Bird-Lore, 9: 93–96.
1570. ———. 1907b. The Baltimore oriole. Bird-Lore, 9: 134–137.
1571. ———. 1918. Three years after. Bird-Lore, 20: 201–210.
1572. Wythe, M. W. 1916. Nesting of the Tolmie warbler in Yosemite Valley. Condor, 18: 123–127.
1573. Young, H. 1955. Breeding behavior and nesting of the eastern robin. Am. Mid. Nat., 53: 329–352.
1574. ———. 1958. The robin's year. Pass. Pigeon, 20: 51–57.
1575. Youngworth, W. 1946. Carolina wren and orchard oriole in Woodbury County. Iowa Bird Life, 16: 65.
1576. ———. 1955. The saga of a cardinal nest. Iowa Bird Life, 25: 58–59.
1577. Zimmerman, D. A. 1960. Thick-billed kingbird nesting in New Mexico. Auk, 77: 92–94.
1578. Zimmerman, J. L. 1963. A nesting study of the catbird in southern Michigan. Jack-Pine Warb., 41: 142–160.
1579. ———. 1966. Polygyny in the dickcissel. Auk, 83: 534–546.

Addendum*

1580. Barlow, J. C. 1967. Nesting of the black-capped vireo in Chicos Mountains, Texas. Condor, 69: 605–608.
1581. Morehouse, E. L. and R. Brewer. 1968. Feeding of nestling and fledgling eastern kingbirds. Auk 85: 44–54.
1582. Tatschl, J. L. 1967. Breeding birds of the Sandia Mountains and their ecological distribution. Condor 69: 479–490.
1583. Walkinshaw, L. H. 1966. Studies of the Acadian Flycatcher. Bird-Banding 37: 227–257.
1584. Martin, S. G. 1967. Breeding biology of the bobolink. M.S. Thesis, University of Wisconsin.
1585. Langille, J. H. 1902. Rose-breasted Grosbeak. Amer. Ornith., 2: 293–297.

* These references are listed in Table 1 but not entered in the tabulations of Tables 1–4.